MEN, WOMEN

AND OTHER

ANTICLIMAXES

Anatole Broyard

MEN, WOMEN

AND OTHER

ANTICLIMAXES

METHUEN

New York / *London* / *Toronto* / *Sydney*

These articles originally appeared in *The New York Times* and *Town and Country*. Acknowledgments and copyright notices appear on page 211.

Manufactured in the United States of America / First Edition

Published in the United States of America by Methuen, Inc., 733 Third Avenue, New York, N.Y. 10017

Designed by Cynthia Krupat

Library of Congress Cataloging in Publication Data

Broyard, Anatole.
  Men, women, and other anticlimaxes.

  I. Title
PS3552.R7915M4   1980   813".5"4   79-20710
ISBN: 0-416-00531-4

To my editors at the Times

who encouraged me

Contents

Contents

Contents

MEN, WOMEN

AND OTHER

ANTICLIMAXES

A Book for

the Depressed

---

*N*ew *York City* people, as F. Scott Fitzgerald might have said, are different from Connecticut people. They have more problems. Compared to life in Connecticut, every moment in New York City is an emergency.

When they see a serene country expression, New Yorkers can't stand it. They've got to involve you in their problems. There are no innocent bystanders in their world.

On my last visit, for example, I was minding my own business in Books & Company on Madison Avenue, browsing among the shelves like a ruminant animal, when a woman came in with a problem.

She approached Burt Britton, one of the proprietors of the place. "I must find a book," she said, "for a man who is depressed."

Problems are Burt's stock-in-trade. He answered without turning a hair. "Cummings," he said. "Give him Cummings."

"Cummings?" the woman made a very pretty business of shifting her weight from one foot to another. She was beautifully got up and wore her hair in a very short crew cut that emphasized her large, wide-set green eyes. "You think that Cummings . . ."

"Some men drink when they're depressed," Burt said. "I drink and read Cummings."

"Cummings." The woman tasted the word, held it on her palate. She did a half-pirouette toward the shelves. Profiled against them, she appeared, in some extraordinary mimesis, to be dressed for a bookstore. Her clothes were in the deep, rich tones of fine cloth or buckram bindings and her shorn head boldly showed her brainpan to the assembled authors.

It was then that Burt noticed me. He saw me simply occupying space, passively poaching on New York City's vitality, breathing up its scant air, without giving anything in return.

"Here," he said, seizing me by the arm and plunging me into the woman's problem. "Make yourself useful."

The woman whose friend was depressed turned her remarkable eyes on me. Throwing off my bucolic air, I assumed the physiognomy of astuteness that Thorstein Veblen ascribes to New Yorkers.

"While it is true," I said, "that Cummings is a consoling poet, we must also consider the possibility that the gentleman in question may not wish to be consoled."

Burt took the cigar out of his mouth. Through his hair, his beard and his aviator glasses, he smiled with the satisfaction of a man who has single-handedly introduced the art of literary controversy into bookstores.

"He may prefer," I said, "to have his depression recognized, shared, enunciated—even enhanced."

The woman everted her lips ever so slightly. It was the first stage in a slow yielding to the soul kiss of ideas.

"It is conceivable," I continued, "that depression is an irreducible part of the dignity of man. The poetry is in the pity. Take away our depression and what are we? A company of giddy-heads, of afternoon men, as Robert Burton observed in his *Anatomy of Melancholy*."

Burt held up his hand in the manner of a traffic cop or a German expressionist actor of the 1920s. "Gently," he said. *"Doucement.* You're fading the dust jackets." He waited for the woman to give him her undivided attention. When she withdrew her gaze, I could feel the draft.

"I'm no critic," Burt said, "just a bookworm, a naïve and sentimental lover. But as I look at it, a poet is a true believer. If he doesn't believe, who does? He's a salesman, his line is life insurance. He's the guy who charms the suicide off the ledge, gives mouth-to-mouth resuscitation."

The woman's mouth moved to meet the poet's. It was a live animal, a sea anemone, opening and closing on the tides of our talk.

"Valéry," I said, "compared the poet to a man who assembles an enormous machine, piece by piece, on a roof, only to shove it down on the head of the unsuspecting pedestrian."

I was going to develop this theme when Burt raised his index finger to his bearded lips. "Why do we wrap the lady in our raw breath? Cummings can say it better than either of us." He went to get the book.

The woman ran her fingers over the shelf in a delicate arpeggio. She fluttered one foot in a *pas de cheval.*

I congratulated her on her haircut. "It requires daring."

She stroked her head as you stroke a cat. "A cut like this requires three things: an absolute faith in your femininity, a total indifference to public opinion and a working knowledge of physical anthropology."

"Be of love a little more careful," Burt read, "than of everything . . ."

"A decent sentiment," I said. "Yet it may be this very

necessity for carefulness that has depressed the lady's friend."

The woman turned her great green eyes upon me. I saw that they had an adjustable intensity, like a three-way bulb. One hundred, two hundred, three hundred watts. Would she go still higher? She blinked, a perfectly choreographed blink.

With a grand jeté, I sprang to the shelves and plucked out Jacques Prévert's *Paroles*.

"The cry of a creature with fingers caught in a door . . . The woman continues her unquiet question, wound impossible to dress . . ."

Burt loosened his neckerchief. "I'd rather learn from one bird how to sing than teach 10,000 stars how not to dance . . ."

"Tell me the truth, stupid and grandiose question . . ."

"Thy body to me is April, in whose armpits is the approach of spring . . ."

"An accounting machine, a love letter writing machine, a suffering machine . . ."

"A pretty girl who naked is, is worth a thousand statues . . ."

"Tell me the truth, I want to know all, tell me the truth . . ."

Burt clapped the Cummings shut. "Wow," he said. "only a book critic would drop those lines on a depressed man. You going to give him *The Romantic Agony* for a chaser?"

"A good idea. Let him study his depression, its structure, its history, its literature. To love is to die a little, and mourning is the only way out of melancholia."

All this time, the woman was never quite still. She moved as if to music, to the plainsong of the titles on the shelves. Pacing a few steps this way and that, a sentinel to our speech, she paused now and again to contemplate the floor beneath her feet as if it were a basic premise. She used the small space of our triangulation, of which she was the apex, with a stunning economy, much as if Margot Fonteyn were to enter upon the floor of a crowded discothèque.

Now she rotated a large ring on her finger. She put a hand to her throat. Suddenly, with a smooth, swift movement like a double *porte de bras,* she took both books and carried them to the counter.

Burt nudged me with his elbow. "Depression is the dignity of man. She really had you going."

"Mouth-to mouth resuscitation. You ought to be ashamed of yourself."

At the counter, the woman was writing with a tiny gold pen in the Cummings. We watched her move down the page, turn it over, resume on the other side. She opened the Prévert and filled the single blank page in a moment. At the door of the shop, she paused and gave us a brilliant *ménage à trois* smile.

Burt took the cigar out of his mouth and looked at it. "Tell me something."

"What?"

"How can that guy be depressed?"

A Ghost

at the Door

When I knew him years ago in Greenwich Village, it was hard to tell whether he was witty or insane. He was one of the first in our crowd to collect pornography for philosophical reasons. He has a fanatical determination to experience things that prevented him from feeling them. After a year of smoking marijuana almost daily, he announced that he had at last succeeded in getting high. Because he preferred to go out alone at night, he used to slip sleeping pills into his wife's after-dinner coffee.

When I married and moved to Connecticut, I hadn't seen him for several years. Then one night, in a heavy rainstorm, he materialized on my doorstep. I say materialized because that's the way it seemed to me. I couldn't imagine how else he could have arrived there.

He looked like a ghost—tall, thin, pale—his hair plastered to his face, his raincoat ragged in a way that suggested not wear, but decomposition. "Hello, man," he said in a toneless voice.

He didn't smile or give any sign that he thought it extraordinary to appear unheralded on my doorstep, fifty miles from New York City. I immediately formed the impression that time did not exist for him. His "Hello, man" was as casual as if we had seen each other just yesterday.

We were never friends, merely acquaintances, and I was not glad to see him. I was not even curious to know why he was there. I wanted to shut the door in his face, but I was conventional enough to find that impossible.

I took his dripping raincoat and draped it over the banister in the hall. When we were seated in the living room, I looked squarely at him without attempting to conceal whatever expression may have been on my face. He met my eyes with an aggressive piety.

I was still pondering the fact of his presence. I lived fairly far from the center of town on a quiet road, and it baffled me how he had got there. I hadn't seen or heard a car, which gave to this visitation an almost supernatural character.

"I'm surprised to see you," I said with deliberate dryness. "What brings you up this way?"

"I'm walking to Boston," he said. "I was tired, so I thought I'd stop in."

It never crossed my mind that he might be joking. It was clear now that he wasn't, and never had been, a wit.

"Boston's a long walk," I said. "Have you any particular reason for walking there?"

He crossed his legs, looking uncritically at his tattered sneakers. "I received a command," he said.

"A command?"

"A command. So I started walking."

"How did you find me?"

"I heard you lived up here," he said, "so I looked in the phone book and asked directions."

It was about eleven o'clock. The children were asleep and my wife had gone to bed early with a cold, but he showed no curiosity about them, or about anything. He was beyond curiosity.

We sat there without a single thing in the world to say to each other because I had no curiosity about him, either. I knew what he was, in a general sort of way: one of those people whose aberration is patterned after cultural fads. I might have felt sympathy for him if he had not dropped so arbitrarily into my lap.

"Would you like a drink?" I asked.

"If you have some ginger ale. Actually," he added, "I'm hungry."

I wasn't sure what was in the refrigerator. "I can make you some eggs," I said.

"Do you have any peanut butter?"

I made him a peanut butter sandwich and gave him a glass of ginger ale. Neither of us spoke while he ate. When his eyes happened to meet mine, there was no click.

"You know," I said, "you'll never make it to Boston in those sneakers. I've got a pair of boots that are much too big for me. Let me give them to you."

He took a swallow of ginger ale. "Leather boots?"

"Yes. They'd be good for walking."

"I can't wear leather."

We fell into another silence. It was like falling into a hole, where we tumbled on top of each other. I didn't ask him why he couldn't wear leather, because I was afraid this would bring out the whole story.

"I was hoping," he said, "that you might put me up."

"Put you up?"

"I'm tired. I'd like to sleep."

I had known from the moment he appeared that it was going to come to this. I had known, too, that I was going to refuse, and now I asked myself why. My unwillingness to have him in my house was instinctive, a blind rising up of my whole being, but I supposed that there were reasons. I looked at him and at myself in one glance, as if we were two arms of an angle. The image, distant as it was, displeased me nonetheless. I didn't want to be connected with him at all.

He was an alien presence, a discordant note, an unknown quantity. He was a walking symbol of irrationality, and all my life I had been reaching for the rational. My wife and children were as much a product of this reaching as they were of love.

Yet I knew that this was not the real reason I was going to send him out into the rain in his decomposing coat and torn sneakers. I was going to send him away because I could not bear the loneliness in his eyes. Insanity has the loneliest look of anything in the world. It made me want to clutch my wife and children fiercely in my arms.

But where was my charity? My charity was elsewhere, that's where it was. A man's home is his asylum, where he is safe from what I saw in that pale face across from me. This was my last refuge, and he had no right to pursue me here.

"I don't have a room for you," I said, in what even he must have recognized as a lie. "I'll drive you to a motel and give you some money."

"I can't drive," he said "I have to walk, and I can't touch money. It's all in the command." He lowered his eyes to the carpet. "I can sleep on the floor."

"You don't understand," I said. "I don't understand you and you don't understand me. That's why we can't sleep under the same roof. You can't explain to me why you're walking to Boston and I can't explain to you why I can't put you up.

All I can say is that we're moving in different directions."

"How about the garage?" he said. "I could sleep out there."

I thought about it. It was inhuman—or rather it was too human—to say no, but I didn't even want him on the property. I felt as if I myself had walked to Connecticut, carrying my future on my back, and I wasn't going to be bullied by somebody else's hallucinations.

"I don't exactly know how to put this," I said, "but I've become the kind of man who doesn't have people sleeping in his garage. If you want me to help you, it will have to be on my terms. You might say that I too received a command."

He stood up. "I thank you for the refreshment," he said.

I helped him on with his raincoat, which was equally wet inside and out. When I opened the door, the rain was falling so heavily that it seemed like a moral statement of some kind.

"You're sure," I asked, "that I can't take you to a motel?"

"It's all right," he said, and he walked into the darkness. I switched on the outside light and watched him until he was beyond it. I felt sorry for him, but not guilty on his account. Each of us was a pilgrim in his own way.

I went upstairs and looked at the children, as I usually did. When I entered our bedroom, my wife stirred. "I heard a noise," she said in a sleepy voice. "Did someone knock at the door?"

"Yes," I said. "A ghost."

"Come to bed," she said. "It's so cozy with the rain beating on the windows."

I couldn't say this to her, but it didn't seem cozy to me. At any moment I felt the rain might come through the windows or the roof and wash away everything we had so carefully put together.

Reflections on an Unphotogenic Childhood

P_{eople} say, "I had a wonderful childhood" or "I had a disastrous childhood," but I know only that I had an unphotogenic childhood. This is my impression after spending the morning looking through an old family album of photographs of myself and my two sisters when we were children. I happened on the album by accident; whatever kind of childhood I had, I would not deliberately have gone back to look for it.

What struck me most was the remoteness of these photographs, the feeling of an immense distance traversed. They were like something from another century. I'm not that old, I reflected. Why do we look so different? I mean different from the photographs of today, from those of my own children?

In the earlier album, you can feel the stillness of the photographs, which is something like the stillness of Sunday morning after church. It was as if we stopped time to take those photographs, and in a sense I suppose we did, because the picture would blur if you moved. Now it seems an odd choice: to have to be still or be blurred. I think the effect would be less uncanny if some of the photos showed nothing but a smear of movement.

My own children were usually photographed in action, busy, playing, in the middle of things. A typical picture shows them at two and four, splashing in a Connecticut stream, naked, laughing and not self-conscious. It is the familiar "candid" shot, in which the children are oblivious of us and the camera.

I wonder now: Were my sisters and I ever unself-conscious or oblivious of our parents? Did we think in terms of "candor"? I'm sure that, except for the traditional infant pose on a white fur rug, we would not have dreamed of allowing ourselves to be photographed without clothes. We felt that it was bad enough to have to show our naked faces. Like primitives, we were afraid of having our personalities sucked up into the camera.

We would not have been able to understand why anyone would want to photograph us playing, for playing was not yet seen as a socially significant activity. For us, a photograph was more like a visit to the doctor, or a preview of Judgment Day. We got all dressed up, scrubbed our hands and faces, tried to look as neutral as possible in order to deny what we could not anticipate. Our chins were generally lifted, as if we were trying to keep our heads above water.

And, of course, we were photographed in black and white. I don't know whether there was color film in those days, but we didn't think of life as colorful; it would not have occurred to us. Nor did we find it necessary to smile; we smiled only when something was funny. Under the searching eye of the camera, we stood up straight, our hands at our sides, our feet together like little soldiers, as in "Onward, Christian Soldiers."

We gazed out of our faces like people who had never seen themselves in a mirror. We did not think of ourselves as having "identities." These photographs were simply "stages on life's way," as Kierkegaard called one of his books. We obeyed the camera as if it were a gun and bore witness to the stealthy passage of time. We had no idea of embellishing the outward appearance of our lives; I believe we felt that you could not lie to a camera, that it would inevitably show you up.

The circumstances of the pictures were determined more by the available light than by any consideration of the environment. We relied on the sun to supply that light, to be the agent of our reproduction. In the earlier pictures, which were taken in New Orleans, the sun was ferocious. In fact, it rather bleached us out, left us looking pale and insubstantial, like dried flowers.

After we moved to New York, when I was six years old, we were always photographed on the roof of the brownstone in which we lived. My father believed that the roof was the only place where there was sufficient light. While he never found it, he never stopped pursuing brightness. He seemed to doubt the potency of the sun in New York and insisted on facing us directly into it. And of course, we frowned and squinted, and as a result our life looked sadder or angrier than it may have been.

My mother never took our pictures, always my father. She disdained mere images; she had produced the originals. Nor, in most instances, would either of my parents enter the photographs themselves, except for my father's shadow at our feet. It was as if they felt that with adulthood their lives were completed and needed no further documentation.

Moving back and forth, side to side, shouting contradictory

instructions, my father fiddled with the lens and peered through the viewfinder. And though we struggled to maintain our neutral expressions, he sometimes took so long that we betrayed ourselves. Every now and then, there is a picture with a personality peering out, like a deer trapped at night in the headlights of a car.

Once we moved to New York, we inhabited, in the family album, a bleak landscape of tarred surfaces, chimneys, tin cornices and clotheslines. People who did not have backyards hung clothes on the roof in those days, and we were posed against sheets, towels, tablecloths, shirts, dresses, nightgowns, pajamas and underwear. My sisters and I were aware of these intimate articles fluttering behind us and this awareness filtered in some subtle way into our attitudes.

Some time ago, Mary McCarthy wrote that the American personality always looked as if it had just had a bad haircut. That was us. We certainly had bad haircuts. After leafing through the old and new albums, I realize how far Americans have come in making themselves look better. Almost every child today seems attractive, or at least passable looking, in his long hair.

I think they have lost something, though, in this cosmetic evolution. With our ears sticking out, our unframed faces, our secretive mouths and wary eyes, we looked as if we realized what we were in for, as if we knew that something difficult was expected of us and that we would probably have to try to do it.

I've been thinking about the family albums of my children's children. I suppose that by their time, there will be nothing but movie cameras, that stillness, especially the monumental stillness of my childhood pictures, will be thought unnatural, a morbid shirking of a child's duty to enjoy himself while he can. Probably there will be television cassettes and the children's first faltering steps—their first everythings—will be repeated in instant replay.

Then, as American life continues its liberating advance, these tapes will be erased and my grandchildren will step out boldly into the future without the embarrassment of a past.

The New York Woman

S*itting* by the window in a coffee shop on 62d and Lexington I admire the women. Now that I live in Connecticut, I come to New York as one goes to an art gallery, to look at the women.

As a former New Yorker, I take a chauvinistic pride in these women that I see. I think of clothes as theater, and in this arena I find our women superior even to their French counterparts. While the Frenchwoman may have an edge in clothes as such, she is no match for the New York woman in the art of imaginative projection. French chic is a fairly rational affair and the American woman's wardrobe is a riot of metaphor, of skeletons in the closet, of a surrealism that was born in France but bred in our boutiques. The New York woman is the scarecrow and the bird of paradise of our sociology. Her theater of the absurd is at least as good as Eugene Ionesco's.

I'm watching such a woman right now, as she walks west on 62d. She exists in that glamorous space between thirty-five and forty-five, and she is obviously unemployed, in this moment at least, in any other job but that of dramatizing herself. I would not be surprised to learn that she is going shopping, seeking to extend and further convolute her image.

She is hatless and her hair is frizzed, which suggests to me that she has just got out of bed, that I am seeing her exactly as she emerged from her unconscious. Her hair hints that she is charged with electricity; it crackles around her head like a halo. It connotes a piquant incoherence, as if all the wires of a switchboard had been pulled out. She is not only uncombed, but unmitigated.

She wears painter's pants—off-white, cotton, wrinkled to a precise degree of casualness. They do not—are not supposed to—fit. They are like thin canvas—and this, of course, is what they are: a canvas for incongruity. You can never wholly know me, she intimates. You can't tell what I might do, where my whimsy will take me. I am your perennial surprise. There is a pun implicit here: woman as painter, a conceiver of scenes and visions, an interior decorator of our entire culture.

With the painter's pants—nonchalantly rolled up as if for emergency, sport or adventure—she wears a pair of $285 boots, to dispel the notion that necessity dictates any of her choices. The boot heels rattle with a suggestion of feudal or military authority, with a soupçon of leather perversion, of extreme contingencies, difficult and dangerous terrain.

The New York woman affects a striped silk blouse, loose-fitting and collarless, rather like an old-fashioned man's shirt, minus the punitive starched neckband. Here again, the connotations teem. Androgyny at home, unbuttoned and easy. She borrows the shirt from men, but disdains the confining collar, the yoke of convention. In the fullness of the blouse, her breasts are mobile but ambiguous in size and shape. She is on the move, not on the make.

A short jacket, opulent, expensive, worn open over the blouse. A gleam of velvet, blood-colored and smoother than skin to the touch. A sniff of the purely sensual to spice her ideology. A scarf, emblazoned with ambiguous heraldry, is her brave pennant or banner. In her bag, if it is faithful to its origins, she carries dispatches. She is a messenger of urgency, of secret and consequential designs. She radiates conspiracy.

The New York woman's coat is wooly and voluminous, as if it might be too big for her, as if in her impatience, she simply seized the first one that came to hand. It insinuates, too, a blanket plucked from her bed to cover a nakedness that is momentarily, imperiously, withheld. In its folds, the coat carries also the history of the cloak, symbol of emotional extravagance and gothic intrigue, of midnight meetings and journeys in disguise.

While she attempts to march—she is the march of events, of time—her high heels cause her to teeter instead toward her entelechy. She leans forward a little, as if to meet her destiny cheek to cheek, her will, her higher determination preceding the nether commitment.

Her lips parted in a pretty gasp, she is breathless with newly minted identity, with the speed of her incessant metamorphoses. Her brows plucked to the dramatic line she scribbles below her signature, her blind eyes fixed on an improbable apotheosis, she advances through the afternoon.

I wonder as I turn my head to follow her up the street, whether she gets the joke, enjoys the comedy of her drama. I can only suppose that some New York City women know exactly what they are doing, and some do not. Like actresses, the good ones play the part for all it's worth and the others simply try to live it.

Famous People
I Have Almost Known

"*Dad,*" my thirteen-year-old son asked, "have you ever met any famous people?"

I was saying good night to him, a ritual I enjoy because he is between sleep and waking and his unconscious comes to the surface. It is a time when we grow philosophical and he asks me to tell him about my Army experiences, or to relate once more how I picked up his mother in the Union Square station of the IRT.

"Famous people?" I said. "What kind of famous people?"

"Any kind," he said. "Movie stars?"

"Well, yes, I have met some movie stars. I met Steve Mc-Queen."

This was promising. *The Great Escape,* starring Steve McQueen, is one my son's favorite movies. "What is he like?"

"Well, the last time I ran into him, he wasn't famous yet. We were at a party in a kind of attic. There was a low steel beam across the ceiling and Steve McQueen hit his head on it."

My son considered this for a moment. "Who else did you know?"

"Well, I met Marlon Brando. He wasn't really established yet, either. I was in a cafeteria with a girl and Marlon Brando came in and said hello to her. Then he caught a fly in his hand and showed us his calluses from his motorcycle."

"Did he squash the fly?"

"No, he let it go. I used to see George Segal a lot before he went to Hollywood. His brother was a friend of mine. George used to do pushups between two chairs because he thought his shoulders were too narrow."

"Didn't you ever meet anybody *after* they were famous?"

"Let me see. Oh, yes. I met Paul Newman after he was famous. It was at a dinner party. Everybody was standing around talking in the living room, but when we started eating dinner, which was a buffet, Paul Newman and his wife, Joanne Woodward, took their plates into the bedroom and sat on the floor between the twin beds in there. Most of the other people at the party tried to sit on the floor in the bedroom, too, but there wasn't enough room."

My son suppressed a yawn. He did it very cleverly, massaging his jaw as if to see whether he needed a shave. I ran ten years of "The Late Show" through my head, trying to think of famous people. "I spent an evening once with Barbra Streisand and Elliott Gould. Her gynecologist was a friend of mine and he invited me over to meet them. I was engaged to your mother at the time, so I took her along."

"Did she sing?"

"Your mother?"

"*Barbra Streisand.*"

"No, she talked."

"What did she say?"

"I can't remember."

"What did Elliott Gould say?"

"Please pass the butter."

My son got out of bed. "Excuse me, Dad, I have to get a drink."

He was obviously giving me a chance to collect my wits. I did. I was ready for him when he came back. "Here's a good one," I said. "I met Norman Mailer."

This got a stir out him. My son and his friends are reading *The Naked and the Dead*.

"Is he pretty tough, like his book?"

"That's just what I was going to tell you. He invited me to punch him in the belly."

"Did you?"

"Well, yes and no."

"How do you mean, yes and no?"

"Well, I didn't exactly punch him. I just gave him a light tap."

"Why'd you do that?"

"I didn't know how hard his belly was and it wouldn't look good, you know, for a book critic to double up a famous writer with a punch."

"How hard was it?"

"Pretty hard."

"Did you invite him to punch you in the belly?"

"No, but he did anyway."

"Did he give you a light tap, too?"

"No, he didn't. Or maybe he thought it was."

"Did you double up?"

"Not really."

My son's eyes grew thoughtful. That never happened when I told him Army stories. I had to do something fast. "You know the famous black writer James Baldwin?"

"We don't read him till the ninth grade."

"Well, I used to know him in New York and then I met him again in Paris. We were in the same restaurant, at different tables. Somebody at his table was telling a joke and when James Baldwin laughed, he threw his head back so far that we saw each other upside down."

This story earned me a sardonic look. Sardonic looks from your thirteen-year-old son are almost as bad as the Oedipus complex. I brought out my ace in the hole: "I met Adlai Stevenson."

"*The* Adlai Stevenson?"

"There was only one."

He waited for me to continue. His face took on an expression of energetic patience. "It was at a wedding reception. There were a lot of people, but when the bride arrived, they all rushed out to greet her, and Adlai Stevenson and I were left alone in the room, this far apart."

"What did you do?"

"Well, I looked at him, you know, but I was so surprised to find myself alone with Adlai Stevenson that I couldn't think of anything to say."

"What did he do?"

"Wait, let me think. . . . He looked at me, then he looked at the floor, and then he put his hands in his pockets."

My son looked at me, then he looked at the ceiling and then he put his hands under his head. "Gee, Dad," he said carefully, "you've certainly had an exciting life, haven't you?"

The Man Who

Danced on Broadway

I was walking along Broadway the other day, and as I
looked around me I tried to imagine what my father had seen
in it. He believed in Broadway, just as he believed in
boulevards. It was necessary for him to think of the city in
which he lived as having a heart. He was a walker who had to
get out into the street and see that the world was there.

We had come from New Orleans, where every man in the
French Quarter was a boulevardier, and life was a musical
comedy. My father was a builder and when the work ran out
we emigrated to New York. He could never conceive of a city
like New York not having work to do.

We lived in Brooklyn, and every Saturday morning my
father would leave my mother and me to go to Broadway. I
think he went there to try to embrace the idea of New York.
We didn't know anybody in Brooklyn, and I suppose he was
forced to grasp at generalities. He would start out at exactly
eleven o'clock and I would stand in the front yard and watch
him as far as the corner. Moving fast, almost dancing, he
twitched his shoulders in his tight jacket until it sat just

right, until some secret sense of fittingness was satisfied. He stood very straight—at five feet nine inches he saw himself as a tall man—and his pants were pulled high on the chest to show off his long legs. He believed he had unusually long legs.

Seeing him hurry away from home, I could sense that he was glad to be by himself. I was too small to keep up with him and my mother couldn't walk, as he put it. She had trouble with her feet, which made me think of mothers as moving very slowly, like glaciers. It was hard to keep out the thought that my father loved Broadway more easily than he loved us.

When he was walking away, especially when he was walking away, there was a kind of jazz in my father's movements, a rhythm compounded of economy and flourishes, functional and decorative. He had a blues song in his blood, a wistful jauntiness he brought with him from New Orleans, where he had been one of the best dancers in the French Quarter. Years later, I asked my mother why he always walked so fast and she said that he wanted to run away once and for all, never to come back, but that he couldn't make up his mind.

It boiled down to a choice between us and Broadway, and every Saturday Broadway won. We never asked him where he went and he never told us, but we knew. While something in his pride kept him from saying, it slipped out in his stories. He was a great storyteller, and that, too, might have drawn him to Broadway. I think of him now, a stranger in a city of strangers, shopping for stories.

What did he do there all day? How did he pass the hours between eleven in the morning and seven in the evening, when he would return as punctually as he had left? Did he watch a double feature in the midday dark, his hat on the seat beside him his only companion? Did he have his glistening shoes shined yet again? I can picture him standing against a building, one foot raised on the box, surveying the street over his cigar.

In the Automat, he eats two fish cakes with tomato sauce and then a bowl of preserved figs. Back on the street, he interrupts his saunter to study haberdashery, knives and scissors, wristwatches and rings, Florsheim shoes like his own. He lingers before a novelty shop to ponder boutonnières that squirt water, papier-mâché dog messes, itching powder and other means to make your friends laugh. Outside the Tango Palace, he coolly examines photographs of the hostesses. In the penny arcade, he plays the slot machines, moves on to the shooting gallery where he knocks down little yellow ducks.

Once, when I was six or seven, before my novelty wore off, my father took me to the shooting gallery. Squeeze, he said. Hold your breath and squeeze. My cheeks puffed out, my hand trembling with joy on the trigger, I squeezed. The rifle made a petulant noise and the duck did not fall. Your father is a crack shot, the attendant said. You'll be a crack shot too, when you grow up.

Could my father have had a broad on Broadway? A woman who waited for him among fringed lampshades, gazing into a compact, wiping with a lacquered fingertip the lipstick crusted in the corners of her mouth? No, not a woman. No woman could have met the expectations expressed in the angle of his hat, the gleam of his shoes, the stickpin thrust though his tie into his heart.

Only Broadway could have done that, with its windows filled with promise, its movie houses blinded with romance, its palaces where the last tango never ended. My father was in love with cities, with boulevards, with a life that eluded him all his life.

Walking along Broadway, I brooded on my father. It was just as well, I thought, that he hadn't lived to see what it became. If he had, Broadway might have made up his mind for him and he would have run away like my mother said.

Send in the Troubadours

W_hat_ we need out here in the country is a revival of the wayfarer. We need minstrels, peddlers, beggars, pardoners, vagabonds and knights. Scribes, tinkers, troubadours, charlatans, gleemen and jongleurs. As J. J. Jusserand says in his classic _English Wayfaring Life in the Middle Ages,_ such men are the "microbes" of society, carrying the germ of human contact from one isolated soul to another.

We have forgotten how to live in the country, to gossip over the fence. I have my acres and you have yours. With all the protective screening, the chain-link fence of evergreen trees and shrubs, I could live here forever without catching sight of a human form. We have quarantined ourselves in privacy, ambushed our conviviality.

For a man like myself who works at home, this vacancy is dispiriting. I'm getting amnesiac, forgetting the terms of the human condition. It goes without saying that my wife, that poor creature who is so widely pitied in contemporary literature and sociology, is rarely under my roof. She is shopping, sailing, skiing, skating, playing tennis, taking dance classes, lunching with friends, visiting a gallery or an antique show, or riding her motocycle. The children, too, are away from home, playing or staying the night with friends whose parents, unlike me, have provided them with all the toys of indulgence that imagination can conceive or money can buy.

Only the dogs are here, but I have pretty much exhausted their conversational repertoire. True, I still talk to them, and they continue to wag their tails and rest their muzzles on my knee. My German shepherd droops her ears in commiseration and my yellow Labrador wrinkles his brow and cocks his head, but it's not enough. While they may be my best friends, a man is one of those unfinished creatures who cannot survive, or prosper at least, without the consolation of another of his species.

I sit here, pencil in hand, staring at parallel lines and yearn for a knock at the door, a chance to exercise the rusty reflex of civility. Suppose, for example, a minstrel were to drop in. He might cheer me with a song of ecology, of condominiums, rising taxes or drug abuse. Fingering his lute, fluting his countertenor, he would harmonize me with the world beyond my foundation planting.

How gladly would I welcome a beggar, someone with even less money than I. They say that beggars can't be choosers: In exchange for food and drink, he would sit and listen to my political opinions, my theories of art, my Army experiences, my unfinished novel. He might even teach me to receive, I who have been schooled all my life only in giving.

If a sly peddler passed this way, I would sharpen my wits against his wiles, enjoy the novelty of hearing something praised, throw off genteel euphemism for a grateful hour. I might also buy some of the things I need, since I can never persuade the people in the shops to wait on me.

Just think what a tinker might do! Drawing on his broad experience and native ingenuity, he would regulate the delicate machinery of the self, slow this and accelerate that, moisten the spirit with a drop of oil, mesh my clashing gears, ease the springs of desire.

A scribe could pay my bills, before my whole life is disconnected. He could answer my letters from readers, thanking the positive ones and vituperating the others in Latin. He could finish my novel for me.

Jusserand never tells us what a gleeman is, but I choose to take the name literally and when he comes, I'll cram my closets, cupboards, and chests of drawers with glee in all flavors.

A jongleur is both an acrobat and a juggler. The acrobat can instruct me in bending with the wind, warping with the age, assuming a contemporary stance. If he can juggle my finances too, I'll buy him a new suit of motley.

I'll call for a knight to champion my cause, slay some of the dragons of the seventies, resuscitate our dying chivalry. Secure in his coat of mail, he might even tell me what masculinity means. If he has a troubadour in his train, that sentimental gentleman might croon a few encouraging words about love, which people out here tend to keep clipped, like their lawns.

A vagabond. I'd like a whole troupe of vagabonds to mock my righteousness and teach me mischief, to show me how to live with risk, swagger a bit, act on impulse, revive the imp of the perverse.

And a pardoner, imagine a pardoner who enabled me to ransom my sins, to escape penance or punishment. Because I no longer know where my sins begin and end, it's just as well that pardoners are not too particular. If I bargain well, he will give me an elastic blessing that will encompass all my morality.

Most of all, and it is hardly necessary for me to tell you this, I long for the comforts of a charlatan or quack, one of those golden-tongued double-talkers who can persuade anyone of anything. I want him to tell me that I will live forever.

The philosopher Vico, who influenced James Joyce, held that history is cyclical. For all I know, the wayfarer may be wending his way back. Since my doorbell doesn't work, I'm going to get a great iron knocker, in the shape of a lion's head. Then I'll sit back and wait.

Love as a

Weekend Guest

W_hile_ my wife wears casual clothes, my friend's girl wears leisure clothes. Her pants are a French copy of United States Army fatigues, and they are altogether fitting, for she is fatiguingly attractive.

I know because he has told me, and because it is obvious, that they are in the first wild stage of infatuation. They have come out to the country to gladden our hearts with their gladness, to add the charm of our house, the sense of open space, to their pleasure in one another.

I have never seen my friend look so well. He seems younger, thinner, handsomer, a thorough renovation of the ironical, self-deprecating character I used to know. In the twelve years since his divorce, he has gone through several comfortable, practical relationships with reasonable women of an appropriate age, but this is his first "girl," the first time he has well and truly fallen, as they say. It's a good word, fall, for that is what he appears to be doing, falling toward this girl like a star.

He is lit up, he leaves a flaming trail. During the introductions, he is almost dancing. As I carry their bags downstairs to the guest room, I feel that they are packed with delight and it gives me a pang. How long has it been since my heart leaped up like a dolphin or a flight of birds?

They have brought a disproportionately expensive gift, because their happiness makes them generous and because they feel that they ought to compensate us for not being them. I heft the jeroboam of champagne and wonder: Shall I break it over her?

The children come in to say hello. They know him, but not her. My eleven-year-old daughter immediately senses what's up and smiles. My thirteen-year-old son shakes hands gingerly with the girl, made shy by the electricity she gives off. Our yellow Labrador, who is a male, ventures a tentative little bark, as at an unidentified animal.

We lunch on cold cuts in the living room, where the fire is going. While I am ordinarily the better talker, my friend is scintillating today. He scatters wit all over us, he crackles with associations. I have noticed that emotional gratification often makes men talkative while their women turn silent and secret.

Besides the ordinary civilities, the girl ventures only a compliment on the house. "It is lovely," she says. "And the furniture is perfect." I would like to return the compliment, to say that she is lovely, that she furnishes my friend's life to perfection.

While she doesn't talk much, the girl's mouth is always alive, her lips opening and closing, chewing on some delicious cud, rippling and curving in the calisthenics of elation. I observe my wife's lips and reflect that married women have quiet mouths.

The fire hisses and pops. My friend and his girl look at it with a proprietary air, as if they owned all the warmth in the world. They too are combustible.

I'm glad for him. It does me good to see him happy. But while I am not competing with his happiness, it is difficult all the same, inhuman in fact, not to covet it just a bit.

I watch my wife to see how she is weathering all this. She seems to be doing fine. I am the only one in our family foolish enough to want to be forever infatuated. She is much too good-looking to be upstaged by the girl. Though she is forty and the girl is in her twenties, my wife is a classic, the kind of woman who will always be attractive, while this girl may hold in perfection, as Shakespeare put it, for but a moment. It is impossible to guess how she will age. One always assumes that flagrantly desirable women burn out early, but this may be the Puritan in us condemning the witch to the flames.

Feeling myself carried away by the sheer spectacle of the girl, I search for balancing considerations. She and my friend, I tell myself, are still only picnickers, people on a holiday. They are tourists of the emotions, while my wife and I are natives. So far, this infatuation of theirs is an indefinitely extended date, a contradiction in terms. They are falling stars and we are the Big Dipper.

When I was in the Army, I learned that there are two kinds of explosives. One has a progressive effect, and this is the kind that launches the rocket or sends the projectile out of the cannon. This is the wife, adding her energy to her husband's. The other kind explodes instantaneously and detonates everything around it. This is the girl. She has blasted my friend sky-high and he hasn't come down to earth yet.

Yes, but there is no denying the force of that detonation, the blinding flash, the tremendous swell and lift of it, the stunning destruction of all structures, all defenses.

Yet I knew that once and no longer wanted it. I remember girls coming down from colleges, spending the weekend. Friday night was delirium. Saturday we were amazed by ourselves. But Sunday, Sunday afternoon, I would wish I had children to play with. When the sun was shining, I could see right through myself and those girls.

I remember the emptiness between fullnesses, the valleys between peaks. I remember the finiteness of affairs.

Still, isn't it nice not to have to take your past, present and future in your arms? To act out a little pantomime of freedom, or of irresponsibility? My friend and his girl are gamblers and my wife and I are investors who have given hostages to fortune. They are a studio and we are a house.

And so I seesaw through the afternoon, counting my riches and estimating my losses. The light is dying in the room and when it is long gone, I will lie in my licit bed and they in theirs. If I had it to do over again, I would do it over again, but there is sadness here, too. When children grow up, they never feel that they have played enough.

Through the window of the living room, we watch the sun go down. It is an unusually striking sunset, and we all get up to look. Suddenly, the girl is eclipsed. I realize that the world is bigger and more beautiful than she is. Thank God.

Spare the Heart

and Spoil the Child

I think it's time we broke our children's hearts. They've had their tonsils out, their teeth straightened and all their shots. Their hearts are the only things we haven't done.

It saddens me to see parents refusing to accept this responsibility, to acknowledge the fact that, in the latest professional thinking, heartbreak is an integral part of preventive medicine. Some mothers and fathers simply hide their faces in their hands; others send their kids out into the world with their hearts on their sleeves.

I don't see how they can do it. A child is never truly weaned until his heart is broken. A heart is a messy thing, and breaking it is like toilet training a little boy or girl, getting their feelings out of diapers. Spare the heart and spoil the child.

The human heart is an atavism, a vestigial hangover from the childhood of the species. Just think of that big, fistlike muscle pumping away: What has it got to do with the flickering nuances of modern life? It floods the feelings to no purpose, like a bath or toilet that's run over. Our off-beat habits call for an off-beat organ, not this drum roll, this insistent, pistonlike apparatus that would be more suitable for a steam engine.

Freud said that the genitalia had failed to evolve in the direction of beauty like the rest of the human body. It's odd that he didn't mention the heart, which accounted for most of his business. What is wholeheartedness, after all, but an obsessive trait with infantile overtones?

All hearts are heavy. It's a parent's duty to try to distribute the weight. Progress is merely a means of improving on nature. Situated in the center of the body, the heart takes on a disproportionate importance, assumes a misleading metaphorical significance. In a purely functional perspective, wholeheartedness may be seen as something of a deformity, rather like those tragic pictures of infants with huge, hydrocephalic heads.

The human animal is such a conservative creature, so resistant to change. Knowing what I do and recognizing the necessity of preventive heartbreak, I still find myself dreading the act. I wish I could leave it to my wife, but because she bore them, I suppose it would be even harder for her than for me. Anyway, heartbreak has traditionally been associated with men.

What frightens me and strengthens my will is the thought of someone else breaking my children's hearts, some callow young man or woman doing it as casually as you break an egg on the edge of a frying pan, breaking them without even being conscious of it. It's a delicate operation, you understand. No one else can do it as efficiently and economically as I could, for I know so well what their hearts are like.

If I put it off, it will be just like the business with my son's feet. When he was a baby, he slept on his belly with his toes pointed in. He looked so cute that way, but his feet stayed turned in and the doctor gave us an iron brace for him to wear at night to straighten them out. He didn't like the brace and he cried, and I couldn't bring myself to force him. Now he has to go through life pigeon-toed.

If I don't break their hearts, I can imagine reality running over them, bursting that inflated organ like a ball that has rolled out into the street. Unless I immunize them now, they'll dash headlong—I was about to write heartlong—against the fact that nobody will ever love them as they are loved now, that love between adults tends to disappear into theory, criticism and sex. And if my children should become parents in their turn, what will they feel, how will their hearts hold up, when they discover that each new generation throws off its family even faster than the last?

Like many fathers, I occasionally have vainglorious fantasies of rescuing my children from some terrible attack—a Bengal tiger, for example. But what is the attack of a Bengal tiger compared to the failure of ambition, the insufficiency of talent, the feeling of having been born into a world whose best years are behind it? What can be more terrifying than the intuition that there may no longer be any absolutes—only relative clauses, ambiguities and empty spaces? I don't say that this is so—only that it often seems that way, feels that way.

It's up to me to get my children ready for all this, to teach them to hope for the worst, to turn their broken hearts to account by becoming avant-garde poets, novelists, psycho-therapists. It goes without saying that a two-part heart is better than one. It permits dual control, a bicameral or dialectical heart, a heart for every occasion. Think of the dynamic relation, the counterpoint, between the two halves. What is wit, when you think of it, but the tickle of the broken edges rubbing together? It's an improvement from the cosmetic point of view as well, because wholeheartedness imparts a certain doglike expression to the eyes, as well as encouraging a nervous instability not unlike the wagging of a tail.

Still, no matter how painstakingly I plan it, I'm not looking forward to the thing, to the moment of breaking when I can feel their hearts squirm, like a bird or fish in my hands, the flutter and wriggle, the suck and slather, the gradual subsiding. I steel myself by recalling my own misadventures, how I had to muddle through life as a disadvantaged person because my parents were too old-fashioned to understand the need. Because they never thought to break it, I've got what you might call athlete's heart and I'll die of it one of these days.

There isn't much time. My son is thirteen and my daughter is eleven. Soon it will be too late. I lie in bed at night, listening to my own heartbeat, and consider ways and means.

The Dream

of Competence

S*omething* there is about a hardware store that stirs
in him a deep, atavistic urge. Everything a man can wield in
his hands is here. A temple to human ingenuity, the hardware
store is consecrated to care, renewal and perpetuation. Just as
living is a continual process of dying for each one of us, so it is
with houses. Every home is suicidal, surrendering itself to
time, weather and human error. The hardware store is the
emergency clinic of rural domesticity, and he is the surgeon.

He has put the city behind him because he cannot lay his
hand on it. It is too abstract, too synthetic, a stage set for a
drama by Beckett. For better or worse, it is too finished. He
prefers to try out his creation in the provinces.

Here, in the country, all things are palpable, each tool on
these shelves has its application. To join, to mold, to smooth,
to shape, to have and to hold. Combining guile and brute
force, he will coax, coerce, clamp, marry and maintain that
which is his. The center *can* hold; things need not fall apart.
What epoxy hath joined together, let no man put asunder.

Adrift in the aisles of his local hardware store, lost in a

dream of competence, he rolls the poetry of tools on his tongue. A ballpeen hammer, an auger bit, a cold chisel, groove-joint pliers. A dovetail saw, spokeshave, rabbet plane. A grass whip, bush hook, pick mattock, cutter maul.

In the city, he was a tool himself, blunted on hard surfaces. Now he is a wielder of tools, man the maker, magic artificer of mythology. His long-baffled wish to square, level, order and secure each thing in its proper place can now commence. He will repair his tragic losses, shore up his defenses with hammer and saw. Casting about a keen eye of appraisal, he prepares to clinch with circumstance, to puzzle out the universe, the secret motions of things. He will come to the rescue, deliver the fell stroke of decision, be the mechanic of his fate.

Overalls—what a happy name. While they are stiff now and homogeneously blue, soon they will be velvety with habit, will take on every hue of the sky. If his work shoes creak, his Ever-Flex Monkey Grip gloves crepitate, all in time they too will soften to a second skin.

In his opposed thumb lies his destiny. How gratefully the tool fits there, like a handshake over a bargain made and sealed. He sees his hand for the first time, the most cunning tool of all, more versatile even than a Swiss Army knife. With two hands, what can he not attempt?

Now that he has his tools, too, he need no longer envy the arcana of the womb and kitchen. His wife has her wizardry and he has his. He feels it is a pity that tools are no longer embellished, as in primitive cultures, with the signs and symbols of sex and fecundity.

While it is still summer, he approaches the woodpile with a benign violence of purpose. He means to be ready when the days draw in and the evenings turn cool. When he raises his ax, it describes a perfect curve, flashes in the sun and refracts his stroke. A connoisseur already, he inhales the sweet smells of the different woods as they splay open to him.

Replacing a fallen stone, he fits it like a key into the dry wall, which is as intricately balanced as a sentence by James or Proust. Holding itself together, the wall restores his slipping faith in cause and effect, which city life had challenged. Stepping cavalierly from his extension ladder, he straddles his house, like a great horse between his legs. Heavy with Cuprinol, the paintbrush caresses the ridge board and the shingles.

In the profound recesses of his basement workshop, he fashions his fantasies in wood, sandpapers them in erotic massage. He pores over Sears and Stanley catalogues as a lesser man might gloat over the pages of *Playboy* or *Penthouse*.

Inside of every butterfingers, there is a mechanic struggling to get out. Behind every no, there's a passionate yes. With his stout crowbar, he will pry, lever and jockey his world into place, impose his will, have his way. He will intervene, conserve the natural order. Every driven nail is metaphor.

Is it possible to prepare for every contingency? Is there a tool for each trial of heart and mind? Can we hold happiness in a vise? Can a keyhole saw carve sadness from the soul? Will a diagonal plier reach the throbbing nerves in the brain? Must repressed impulses be pruned? He will scrub himself free of guilt and regret with a Broadway washboard. Pump oil will lubricate the rusty vestiges of desire.

A coat of paint covers a multitude of sins. He will line up his family on the lawn and slosh them with gaiety. He will smooth them, soothe them, miter their dissimilar edges, clamp them forever close. Crouching beneath their heavy-gauge tarpaulin, they will thrill to the thunder and lightning of the tangible.

The Woman Who Was a Perfect Gentleman

"*My trouble*," my friend said, pushing her hair back from her face, "is that I've always been a perfect gentleman with the men in my life.

"I had a strong father and he taught me to be independent, or androgynous, as it's called today. He saw to it that I valued myself, that I developed a sense of dignity. I don't think he realized what a terrible disadvantage this would be for me later in life. He didn't see that he was denying me all the vulgar pleasures of being a woman. And you know as well as I do that those vulgar pleasures are a woman's usual allotment.

"For example, I'm incapable of behaving in a jealous manner. In spite of myself, it's beneath me. But of course you're free, old man, I'm obliged to say when someone is unfaithful to me. What you do is entirely your own affair.

"It isn't, of course. It's our affair, if we're having one, but I can't say that, it's against the rules. We don't press claims in the club, the bylaws expressly forbid it."

My friend sipped her drink. "I was a perfect gentleman about my divorce, and look where it's left me. I work late most nights and free-lance on weekends to send my kids to school. My husband could have easily spared another $10,000 a year, but I was too gentlemanly to insist. I practically shook hands with him in court. You would think we had just finished a round of squash at the Racquet Club.

"Maybe that's why he divorced me. I suppose it was a terrible trial for him, living with a woman who was more of a gentleman than he was. At times, I must have made him feel like a homosexual."

She smiled at the thought, a smile like a mixed drink of irony and sadness. "Think of all the things I denied that man! Scenes, tears, accusations, recriminations—the staff of life. The bread and butter of intimacy. You remember Rodolphe, in *Madame Bovary,* what he said about Emma? Poor thing, he said, she gasps for love as a carp gasps for air on the kitchen table. A good line, isn't it? That's what a proper woman offers a man, a chance to get off good lines.

"When my husband misbehaved, he wanted me to misbehave back, so that he could compare our behavior and feel that his was superior. How much nicer it is to act than to react. Women are usually given the secondhand emotions, the feelings that depend on somebody else's doing something first.

"Regression is the spice of conjugal life. After the honeymoon is over, the husband reverts to his bachelor habits of improvisation, of obeying his impulses, whether this means drinking late with the boys or winking at the girls.

"A normal wife will regress with him. She'll throw a tantrum, withhold her favors, perhaps even threaten to retaliate by taking a lover too. She will stage a little drama, stir things up. This breaks the monotony, serves as a second courtship, gives everybody a fresh part to play.

"Behaving badly is a vacation from the self, a safari into the jungle of tooth and claw, the rain forest where snakes hang from the trees and the ground underfoot is a compost of desire. It's one of the luxuries of civilized life, a grand decadence of perished swans, as the poet said.

"But with a gentleman for a wife, there is none of that. Who wants to kiss a stiff upper lip? My good manners are a mustache, a muscular development that is unbecoming in a woman. Frailty, thy name is woman! Oh, how sweet it is to fracture frailty, to clast icons. And then to put the pieces back together.

"Every man is a tinkerer, a little boy taking his toys apart and putting them back together. But he can't do that with a woman who's a gentleman. She is one of those antiquated toys, made of iron or some impenetrably hard wood, a toy that's all in one piece and won't come apart."

We ordered more drinks. My friend shook out a cigarette and when I picked up the matches and lit it for her, she gave me an affectionate, sardonic look. "A woman's weapons," she said. "I have no woman's weapons. My well-meaning father disarmed me. Did he suppose I would have to do with men like him? That I would fall in love with a gentleman?

"It's too late for gentlemen. The sun has set on the British Empire and the elephant exists only in game parks. As T. S. Eliot observed, a religion needs a society behind it. Being a gentleman is a religion—it certainly can't be recommended on secular grounds—but there's no society behind it anymore.

"In my case, I suppose virtue will have to be its own reward. I'll rehearse my peculiar rituals, like an old-fashioned dancing master in a school without pupils. I'll waltz my good manners around to the music of a broken record."

My friend stubbed out her cigarette as if it was an eraser and she was rubbing out a word in the ashtray. I wondered which word.

"But I'm not being a gentleman now, am I, bending your ear with this balderdash. Listen to that: even my vocabulary is archaic." She looked up into my eyes. "What do you think? Is it too late for me to change? I'm only forty-one.

"I used to be good in school, maybe I can still learn." She smiled. Her smiles are a history of the twentieth century. "Let me see if I know the drill." She stretched her head forward on her neck, like the women in Picasso's *Guernica*. "Hug me, kiss me," she said. "Seize me, squeeze me. Take me, break me, slake me."

Our waiter was passing by. He stopped. "Did you want something, ma'am?"

Environments

W_{hen} *I* was a bachelor in New York City, I saw a little boy of three or four pedaling a blue plastic automobile along the sidewalk of 57th Street between Lexington and Park Avenues. It was about 9:30 on a weekday morning and the street was dense with people going to work. The day was dark and wintry and the sight of that solitary little boy threading his way through the crowd, unaccompanied by a parent or friend, filled me with such sadness that I followed him around the block. Watching him begin a second tour, I said to myself that I would never let this happen to my son.

Now I have a son and I wonder. Is he any better off, any less isolated, on his bicycle on our road in the country, where his nearest friend lives a mile away and the few adults he sees are in blue plastic cars of their own? Was it mere sentimentality, an unexamined prejudice in favor of the pastoral, that led me to pity that little boy on 57th Street?

"We moved to the country for the sake of the children."

"How can you live in the city with kids?"

One hears such remarks all the time as statements beyond

question, yet I think we ought to question them. We ought to ask ourselves what a child may be missing by living in the country and then think about how we might repair some of those omissions.

"New York City is exciting."

This is another statement one hears, from people who have lived in the most beautiful and sophisticated capitals of the world. In choosing the country, are we protecting our children from excitement? Are we condemning them to a calisthenic life in an extended playpen?

We say that we live in the country, but exurbia is not country. It is, in my case at least, a grandiose housing project with almost none of the pastoral values or forms that the word country used to suggest. In my darker moods I feel that I inhabit a void with trees. Few of us live off the land or have any necessary relation to it. We learn no great moral lessons from the land. We are not a link in "the great chain of being." We merely reside here, in a benign exile from the city, in a landscape that strikes us as so undifferentiated that we feel impelled to punctuate it with pools and tennis courts.

I try to imagine what the country means to my son. Is it a window display of the good life? Are all the trees Christmas trees? Or do the stone walls and the split-rail fences constitute a prison? Is nature a blank page or a speaking presence? Is he less or more isolated here than that little city boy was on 57th Street?

We tell ourselves that the city is dangerous. So it is, but there are all kinds of dangers. An excessively sheltered life may be dangerous, too, in terms of the development of sensibility, of resourcefulness, of tolerance, of toughness.

Freud observed that life loses interest for us when we cease to risk it. He meant risk in the sense of facing new challenges, even new anxieties. He felt that our personalities develop in response to risk. In this context, I wonder whether I am protecting my son against danger or against risk. I may even be protecting him against life.

Perhaps life sometimes has to hurt us, to pinch us awake. While I am not saying that exurban life does not have its share of pain, I sometimes suspect that these hurts are too exclusive, too internal, too often originating in the family. Much as it worries me, it may be healthier to have the outside world hurt my son. He may interpret it more realistically, more philosophically, if the hurt comes from them and not us. The nuclear family may be too nuclear in the country, where, until a boy drives a car, most of his human contact occurs at home.

Like most parents, I want my son's life to consist of only ideal experiences, yet I know that such a life would turn him into a monster of complacency. Every Utopia has its Frankenstein monster. Only trial and error can compose what Wordsworth called "the deeper music of humanity."

Then there is the notion of street sense, or gutter wisdom, hard-won insight into the way things are. While I am not sure about the wisdom to be found in today's gutters, there are other mysteries that have survived the hard surfaces of the street.

There is the mystery of human variability, for example. On a New York City street, a boy can see a captain of industry, a beggar, a chic woman, a drunk, a poet, a madman, a prostitute, a dancer. People are the best entertainment and the best education, while the country boy's gutter wisdom is only TV.

I remember that the little boy on 57th Street was smiling, a secret, inscrutable smile, as if he saw something that he was saving up to think about later. He was enjoying his tour and he did not appear to feel lonely. While not many of the pre-occupied people in the street noticed him, I got the impression that he was aware of them. Perhaps I exaggerate, but it is possible that he was regarding them with what was the beginning of a sense of irony.

Perhaps one needs the sight of many people in order to develop a sense of irony. What is there on a country road that would stimulate it? The same is true of a tragic sense of life, or the instinct of politics.

I ask myself whether, in moving to the country, I have not attempted to move away from the present, as well as from the city. Many of us who live out here see the country as a return to something, a going home again. But what do we go home to? What has survived in the country except a few saltboxes?

Exurbanites may place too high a value on innocence. In a backlash against the stultifying sophistication of our time, we may be raising our children as dumb animals. And sheep may safely graze in the country. Do we want our children to be sheep? Is innocence a virtue, or a benign form of brainwashing?

I don't mean to romanticize the incidental uglinesses of city life. While ugliness has its part in the polyphony of things, one can have too much of it, just as one can be exasperated by prettiness. The growing vandalism by country boys may be a protest against the prettiness of their environment.

It is another of the ironies of life that we seem to learn from ugliness and take prettiness for granted. Our children sit in our landscapes, in our tastefully furnished houses, and search for the city's ugliness on television. Unfortunately, it is usually silliness rather than ugliness that they find, and even television's occasional evocation of evil is generally falsified.

Here, at last, is the question that worries me most: Is the relative innocuousness of growing up in the country an incubation period for faith or for disillusionment? Am I raising a pet, a noble savage, a hick, or a boy whose secure sense of himself will survive the city, if necessary, and the world?

When an
Invitation Isn't . . .

"*We were* thinking of dinner," she said.

"Yes?" I said, cradling the phone on my shoulder.

"You know, like four compatible people sitting down together and eating something."

"OK."

"Maybe something exotic, maybe ethnic—or we could play it straight."

"All right."

"It might be pleasant."

"Of course."

"I realize it's not a very original suggestion," she said, "but you've got to eat somewhere."

"That's true."

"It locks us in a little—we invite, you and your wife accept, we eat—but it's still a nice scene, don't you think?"

"Sure."

"Like how many things can four people do together?"

"It's an interesting question."

"It goes without saying," she said, "that I'm assuming

everybody's energy is still up for the idea. We can check out the rhythms later."

"Fine."

"It's too early now to make a commitment, so let's just consider this an exploratory call, a feeler."

"Naturally."

"There's nothing worse, if you're not with it, than altering the flow, the ongoing direction, and trying to lean the other way."

"It is hard."

"So we'll keep it fluid for now."

"We can even have a fluid dinner."

She laughed, a perfunctory little laugh. "You know, we'd really love to see you, but I'll confess something to you because I know you understand me. In a way, deep down inside, I dread dinner. There's something so *déjà vu* about it. I ask myself, is that it? Is that what it's all about, to eat dinner every night?"

"You want to forget about it?"

"No, no. I'm just contacting the fact of dinner. Right now, at this moment, I see the whole thing as a stab at closure, a cheap gestalt. You want to shape the shapeless, you call up somebody for dinner. What happened to our spontaneity? Where are all the vectors?"

"I think," I said, "that you're too hard on dinner. After all, there are some very pretty polarities. Someone makes it and someone eats it. And then you can't beat dinner for focus."

"Focus, yeah. Too much focus, if you ask me. I always feel so regressive eating, so unsublimated. It's almost as bad as going to the bathroom."

"I don't agree. I look at dinner as a way of being-in-the-world, of engaging the tangible. As Lévi-Strauss said, it all comes down to the raw and the cooked. Symbolically, dinner is ritual, but substantively it's real. You can also work with it as feedback. While you eat, you can ingest the impact of the other diners."

"But don't you find the whole thing deflecting? I mean, to have your mouth full for a whole hour. I feel so vulnerable, so disarticulated, when I can't talk."

"Your approach," I said, "is too body-oriented. Try to imagine a metadinner, not so much a filling occasion as a fulfilling one."

"I used to dream about teeth. Either they were falling out or they turned into tremendous fangs."

"Use that," I said. "Use it. You could treat dinner as a working out of that fantasy, as an opportunity for assertive biting."

"You know," she said, "you would have made a marvelous therapist. Have you ever thought of it?"

"From time to time. But I'm afraid that if I were to make peace with my narcissism, it might block my creativity."

"Oh, no," she said. "I'm sure you'd resonate to your clients. You're a very contrapuntal person."

"Eight hours a day of *einfuhlung.* It could be depleting. But we were discussing dinner, the ontology of the institution."

There was a pause. "Dinner be damned. All I really care about is intimacy—intimacy as an aesthetic construct—and then I find myself sweating in a kitchen."

"Stop calling it dinner. Restructure your feelings until you can accept dinner as an infusion, an act of nonverbal communication, body English, oral gesturing, motor synchronicity. Women have turned dinner into a repetition-compulsion and you have an obligation to yourself to reformulate the contract."

"The more I think about it," she said, "the more I hate it. When everybody's gone home, I always feel like a dirty plate, like a coffee cup with a cigarette butt floating in it."

"Making dinner," I said, "may well be the root cause of female paranoia. But you have to remember that dinner can also be an aggression, a penetration, if you like. It doesn't have to be a passive serving-up of the self. Cannibalism is the bottom line of love. Dinner is also a political situation. Historically, it has always been rigidly structured in terms of precedence. It is place, presence, status, not pot roast, that you serve up. When you break bread with someone, it crumbles into possibility."

She was silent. I could hear her fingernails drumming on the phone. A sigh came through, like the sound in a seashell. "I wonder," she said slowly, "whether it's not too late for dinner. I don't mean tonight, I mean too late—too late in history. Perhaps the moment for dinner is past. Perhaps we can no longer relate to it. The whole idea, persisting through time, is so . . . so massive."

"Would you rather go to a restaurant?"

"A restaurant?" she said. "Well, that's a thought. I like the neutral space of a restaurant, the feeling of figure-ground, the otherness of the others."

"Is it a deal then?"

"Well, let's not be unilateral. Ask your wife to call when she comes home. I'd like to get her associations."

Anaïs Nin's Party

and Mine

Many years ago, I went to a party at Anaïs Nin's house on 13th Street in Greenwich Village. I was very young and rather impressed by Miss Nin. Hers was my first full-scale literary party and its smallest details still stand out in my memory.

I was surprised, therefore, in reading Volume Four of the paperback edition of her *Diary*, to find myself, on page 182, saying and doing things of which I have no recollection. I am described, for example, as dancing with Miss Nin, a pleasure I distinctly remember denying myself out of diffidence.

After dancing with her, I am reported to have said to the girl who brought me to the party, "Anaïs is sensual." According to the *Diary,* the girl answered, "No, Anaïs is mystic." I countered with, "No, Anaïs is sensual. Or perhaps a harmony of both."

While I was pathetically eager to cut a figure, it is difficult for me to imagine myself saying these things. I was too much in awe of Miss Nin to pronounce on her sensuality. In fact, sensuality was not one of the things I noticed about her. There were too many other aspects intervening.

Nor do I recognize the diction as mine. "Perhaps a harmony of both": that particular turn of phrase suggests someone who speaks several languages. Also, I don't believe I was aware at the time of the harmony between the sensual and the mystic.

Was Miss Nin being kind in her *Diary*? She may have thought to protect me against the notorious absurdity of youth, the vulnerability of an untried boy who was out of his depth. For all I know, since it now seems that my memory is not infallible, I might have said, "This is a nice apartment," or, "Were you troubled by rats when you lived with Henry Miller on a houseboat in the Seine?"

It is possible that Miss Nin was indulging in poetic license. If I had known that she wanted poetry, I would gladly have accommodated her. I was steeped in the works of Wallace Stevens in those days, and there were all sorts of serviceable things I could have brought into play.

I might have said, "Life is an old casino in a park," or, "I have wiped away moonlight like mud."

While we were dancing, Miss Nin might have said, as she did somewhere in her *Diary*, "Think of the ballet exercises. The hand reproduces resistance to water." She might have said, "It is art which is ecstasy, which is Paradise, and water."

I would have replied, "My titillations have no footnotes / And their memorials are the phrases / Of idiosyncratic music."

I can hear her murmuring, as if to herself, "It is possible I have never learned the names of birds in order to discover the bird of peace, the bird of paradise, the bird of the soul, the bird of desire."

And I'd come right back with, "Canaries in the morning, orchestras/ in the afternoon, balloons at night."

I wish we had danced. I console myself with the thought

that, while I do not recall it, we may have. I see us doing a tango. We draw ourselves up to our full height, stare profoundly into each other's eyes. Miss Nin's are black, impenetrable. Is she thinking of something else, of the tango as a metaphor?

Our knees are flexed. Her right hand is flattened against my left. It is small, white and dry. Her left hand grasps my shoulder in an astonishingly powerful grip. My right hand is splayed in the arch of her back.

We step out sideways, like Egyptian frontalistic sculpture. We take long, swooping steps, snap our heads right, left, right, plunge into a peristaltic turn. Our deep, forward dip is a dying fall.

The tango is "Caminito." A woman sings in a hoarse, desolate voice *"Que tiempo ha borrado / Que juntos un día / Nos viste pasar."* Miss Nin's eyes glitter. They are sad, wise, bottomless.

The next record is a rumba. Miss Nin's expression is intense, almost painful. Her slender hips swivel to the beat, one-two, one-two. I see that her lips are moving. She can't be counting? It appears to me that her feet are not quite synchronized with her hips. The rumba is an extraordinarily complex harmony of the sensual and the mystic.

Ah, now she has it: everything meshes. She even shakes her shoulders. The effect, however, is not Latin, not rumbalike. Her movements strike me as intellectual, even doctrinaire. Someone on the record cries *"Agua!"* With a gesture of impatience, Miss Nin breaks off the dance.

We march across the room in a fast one-step, our bodies locked in rhythmic determination. Miss Nin pumps her elbows ever so slightly. I march forward, forcing her back. She surges forward, forcing me back. An end table and a lamp crash to the floor. The other couples press themselves against the wall to make way for us.

We walk out on the terrace to cool off. Miss Nin plies a Japanese fan. A man called Dick, who has been cruelly rejected by Pablo, makes an insincere attempt to throw himself from the terrace. It is just as the *Diary* says. A man called Vincent seizes Dick around the waist. He looks inquiringly at Miss Nin, afraid of committing a faux pas.

The girl I came with appears on the terrace. She seizes me around the waist, as if I, too, were about to throw myself off. "Let's go, gigolo," she says. She is drunk.

I am obliged to carry her down the stairs. While she is admired for her seventeen-inch waist, the girl weighs 116 pounds. I am used to carrying her up, rather than downstairs. She has a bad heart and has been warned by her cardiologist that climbing stairs can kill her. Whenever we go anywhere, I carry her up the stairs. I once carried her up the grand staircase in the Metropolitan Museum of Art.

Some months later, the girl will confess to me that she does not have a bad heart, that it amuses her to be carried. But as I don't know this yet, I walk to Seventh Avenue with her in my arms.

It is early in the morning. A taxi passes and I try to flag it by raising the girl as high as I can. It doesn't stop. When another taxi ignores us quite a while later, I drape the girl, whose eyes are closed, on the hood of a parked car.

She opens her eyes. She looks over her shoulder to see where she is. Stretching out her arms, palms down, she embraces the car. "Hey," she says, "I'm sensual." "Nay," I say, "You're mystic. Or perhaps a harmony of both."

Me and My Handyman

P_{eople} in New York City have psychotherapists, and people in the suburbs have handymen. While anxiety in the city is existential, in the country it is structural. A therapist helps you hold your life together, and a handyman holds together your house. To move to the country is to transfer paranoia from people to things. And things are even less permanent, less reliable, than people.

Every house is a house of cards, a system of fragile and temporary supports against the implacable forces of nature. We who live in the country, who inhabit these flimsy bulwarks against time and fate, pray that they will outlast us, that they will prevail against heat, cold, wet and dry, against the frost-heave and settling of earth's fluttering bosom, against insect and animal ravage. But most of all, we pray that our houses will survive what someone comprehensively called the innate contrariness of matter.

The temptations of St. Anthony in the desert are nothing next to the tribulations of a homeowner in the country. If you want to live by Aladdin's lamp, you need a genie when it comes to the rub. My genie is a genial gentleman named Frank. His areas of competence include carpentry, painting, stonework, gardening and marriage restoration.

In fifteen years, Frank has rescued my marriage more times than I can count. The last time was when my wife decided that she could no longer cook the family's hamburgers or franks and beans on anything but a six-burner, double-oven Garland stove with a thirty-inch grill. A Garland is a heavy-duty restaurant stove of stainless steel. It weighs more than eight hundred pounds and costs $1,200, not counting hood, fan, delivery and installation. It is about half as big as most kitchens.

I appealed to Frank. "How would we get it in here?" I asked sarcastically. "We'd have to tear out the whole wall."

My wife and I both looked at Frank. He shrugged. Between his thumb and forefinger, he broke off a piece of the wall. "Plaster's rotten anyway."

In our first house, my wife asked me to have Frank trim back an immense blue spruce outside the kitchen window so she could enjoy a view of the field while she was opening cans.

"Trim that tree!" I exclaimed incredulously. I was fresh from the city and filled with reverence for growing things. Turning to Frank, I said, "Can you imagine anyone wanting to trim that beautiful tree?"

Frank shrugged—he always shrugs. "Don't make much difference. It's dying anyway. " All of his sentences end in anyway.

Like our present house, which is more than two hundred years old, Frank is an advertisement for old-fashioned inde-structibility. A medium-sized man in his middle sixties, he can drive a three-inch nail with two strokes—left- or right-handed. When I gather round the hearth with the neighborhood gentry and we brag about our handymen, I generally ask them whether their man can balance, straight-up, a fully extended forty-foot ladder—using just his wrists.

It goes without saying that Frank is too much of a perfectionist to work with anyone else. He always comes alone, and if the job turns out to require another hand, he courteously accepts me as his assistant. He feels that what I lack in skill, I make up in determination, because it is my house. My incessant worrying also has the effect of making Frank feel optimistic.

He is a morning person and generally arrives with the sun, just before my REM sleep is about to begin. And though I am often late for deadlines, airplanes and first-run movies, I am never late for Frank, because I've got to show him that I'm good at something. Actually, our relationship extends beyond the practical, to the poetic. Just as American technology enabled us to make a moon shot, so Frank's reassuring presence encourages me to dramatic flights I could not otherwise attempt.

There was the time, for example, when the family drove down from Martha's Vineyard one wet night to find that we were locked out. I don't carry a house key, for the same reason that I never carry coins: I can't fit them into my jeans. My wife didn't have her key, either. She is a dancer and likes to call attention to her creativity by disarming little bouts of absent-mindedness.

My children, whom we had already awakened, were waiting for me to rise to the occasion, to solve the problem in a manner that would provide a model for them all through their lives. My wife stood apart, as if to say, "This is where we separate the men from the boys." In the back of the station wagon, both of our dogs began to bark.

I looked at our two-hundred-year-old door, with its wide

boards and beautiful patina, and I knew what I had to do. I kicked it, just like in the movies. It took two kicks to bring it down, and even as I delivered them, I planned to call Frank in the morning. It was worth it: The children clapped their hands, the dogs stopped barking, and my wife said, "Now carry me across the threshold."

Of course, there are times when I wonder whether I am really cut out for the role of country squire, when I throw stones in the pond and mutter about building a stainless-steel house. Instead of climbing up on the roof in a fifty-mile gale to tar a leaking chimney, I could spend my Saturday or Sunday mornings reading the poems of John Berryman or listening to baroque music played on the original instruments.

But I suppose a stainless-steel house would be giving in, surrendering to the creeping pragmatism that is eroding the quality of life. Besides, I would miss my conversations with Frank, the fugal rise and fall of our voices, punctuated by the popping of beer cans, as we shake our heads over the shoddy materials and standards of the times.

Owning an old house is rather like belonging to a fundamentalist faith, and Frank is my preacher. He believes in the true, the square and the level. He reminds me that, no matter what Thorstein Veblen said, the instinct of workmanship is *not* dead. After he leaves at mid-day, I stagger off to take a nap, then when I get up I plug in my electric pencil sharpener and sit down at my desk like a man who knows what it means to do a job of work.

Growing Up

Irrational

"You're being irrational," my wife said to me the other day as I was raising hell with the children.

"Of course I am," I said. "I'm their father, am I not?"

"What does that mean?" she asked.

"It means exactly what it says," I answered. "What is a father if he is not irrational?"

My wife sighed. She recognized the signs.

"I wish you would try," I said, "to cultivate a little irrationality yourself. You can't bring up children on vitamins alone."

She closed her eyes as I warmed to my theme. "How do you expect them to develop personalities if we always behave in a rational manner? Do you want them to grow up to be model children, like model airplanes? If parents didn't behave irrationally once in a while, where would we get our poets and novelists?"

My wife went out to dig in the backyard, which is one of her repressed, almost useless forms of irrationality. I remained in the house to brood on the modern, or rational, family, which I find unsettling.

It appears to me that the family is losing its mystery, its mythology, its theater, that it is trying to turn itself into a controlled experiment in the raising of children. The passion of parenthood is giving way to the dispassionate, and if the trend continues, children will soon be left with nothing to worry about.

What will happen to them, poor little things, growing up in a land of perpetual sunshine, a world without shadows? I can imagine an entire generation deprived of a tragic sense of life, kids who will never have known what it means to be frightened, to be the victim of injustice, of mere caprice, of suffocating, unearned devotion. They'll never be surprised by anything, ambushed by happiness or sadness. They will see everything coming, develop a sense of *déjà vu* before they're ten years old. They may forget how to laugh or cry.

When I see loose groups rationally moving through life and calling themselves families, I want to say, "You're not a family. You're a team. A committee, a club, a caucus."

It wasn't that way with me. I *descended* from my mother and father. I was *extracted* from them. Today we are asked to see the whole world as an extended family, but in my time it was just the other way around. My parents were a conspiracy, a plot against society, which they felt as a continuous pressure to assimilate or new-fangle us. Where I grew up in Brooklyn, every family was ethnic, from a country of its own devising. We were not yet homogenized into Americans.

Our house was an asylum, where we lived out our private lunacy, our peculiarities. In its brownstone confines, we were safe, beyond the reach of those others, just as fugitives from the law once found asylum in churches, where they could not be seized.

The only trouble, as far as I was concerned, lay in the fact that my family insisted on going out, and on taking me with them. I dreaded these excursions, these escapades. To me, they were like a suicide pact. Didn't my parents know that the world was just waiting for a chance to come between us?

Inside, we were a family, but outside we were immigrants, bizarre in our differences. I thought that people stared at us, and my face grew hot. At any moment, I expected my father and mother to expose their tribal rites, their eccentric anthropology, to the gape of strangers.

Anyone who saw me with my family knew too much about me. Nobody is so secret about his loves as a boy of six or seven. Why, I wouldn't even confess my infatuation for a girl on the block, and here I was, exhibiting in public the most intimate relationship I was ever to know.

To go out with my parents was to suffer for the second time the trauma of birth. My mother, who was mildly stout, might as well have been the Venus of Willendorf, a primitive fertility figure. My father was a rogue male, a creature of such reckless masculinity that I always thought of him as breaking the law.

While I loved them, I was uneasy about our relationship. It struck me as a terrible incongruity, especially for a boy, to have originated in my mother's belly. It was such a derivative way for me to have arrived in the world. I would rather have been store-bought, instead of homemade.

My father flustered me more than my mother, for on him fell the full weight of patriarchy, and he was not a man to shirk it. I remember in particular a boat ride to Bear Mountain. This being a sporting occasion, my father elected to wear a pair of plus fours, or knickers. He even went so far as to pull a beret, another installment in his unpredictability, over his unruly hair. Walking beside him, I shut my eyes, guiding myself by the sound of the metal taps on the toes and heels of his brown-and-white wing-tip shoes.

We had come up from New Orleans, where I was born in the French Quarter. For a *bel homme*, a *galant*, like my father, it was no simple matter to walk along the street. He had to strut, stretching and swiveling his head on his neck, arching his back and undulating his shoulders, flourishing his arms in counterpoint to his legs. I would watch him out of the corner of my eye and despair. I half-expected him to break into the Camel Walk, the Shimmy Shewobble, the Black Bottom or the Mess Around.

I wanted desperately to run away from home. My mother and father were too folksy for me, too colorful. Conformity is the first passion of small boys. Originality, if it comes at all, arrives much later. My love for these two misfits, these character actors, was too heavy to bear.

Eventually, I ran away to Greenwich Village, where no one had been born of a mother and father, where the people I met had sprung from their own brows, or from the pages of a bad novel. We buried our families in the common grave of the generation gap, silenced them with the so-called failure of communication. Parents became our shtick, a whetstone for our wit. Orphans of the avant-garde, we outdistanced our history and our humanity.

I became an amnesiac, a flimsy Frankenstein monster of pop sociology. I saw myself as spawned by time, as flies were once thought to be spontaneously generated in offal. I deracinated and rationalized my image. For my new friends and me, parents had become synonymous with the establishment, an outmoded, authoritarian and absurd institution.

Like every great tradition, my family had to die before I could understand how much I missed them and what they meant to me. When they went into the flames at the crematorium, all my letters of introduction went with them.

Now, in my middle age, I understand at last that personality is a conspiracy. I'm grateful to my mother and father for their quirkiness, for this gave me a glimpse of the range of styles, the richness of being. I thank them for their irrationality, which was a grand tour of unmapped territories. Especially, I love them for not being modern, not dumping me into the polluted river of progress before I was ready to protect myself.

Now that I have a wife and family of my own, I've begun to feel what it is. When we go out together, I do my own share of strutting, and I wonder how my children feel about it. Am I an embarrassment to them, or an accepted part of the human comedy? Have they joined my conspiracy, or are they just pretending? Do they understand that, after all those years of running away from home, I am still trying to get back?

Bathrooms

I think I've reached a "passage" in my life. Overnight, I've become the sort of person who cannot be happy without a luxurious bathroom.

A Jacuzzi whirlpool, a showerhead that massages, a sauna, a double-sized vanity sink with a three-way mirror, vast storage spaces crammed with protein-rich soaps, shampoos, water softeners, skin bracers, colognes—I find myself yearning for these things, and I wonder what sort of dread symbolism my bathroom has assumed.

My house is old, circa 1700, my bathroom even older. If you multiply a dog's age by seven to approximate its human equivalent, then a bathroom's age should be ten times that of the house.

A forty-year-old bathroom like mine works out to be four hundred. But while antiquity has its charm, that is not the place for it. On the contrary, a bathroom is the clinic where we wash away all signs of time and mortality.

Because of a steep saltbox roof, I have to stoop in my bathroom. I start out my day on bent knees, and this cramps my spirit, puts a ceiling on my aspirations, forces me to adopt a low profile.

I read somewhere that fleas are trained for circuses by being placed in a Petri dish, a flat-topped glass container that teaches them that jumping doesn't pay. It's the same with me. Where are my grand leaps in the morning, when I am most disposed to make them? I want to wake up in a cathedral. A truly modern bathroom *is* a cathedral.

I try to find the poetry in my archaic bathroom. It is cozy, snug, quaint, a museum of American eccentricity. But it isn't. It's drafty, knobby, harsh, a hangover from the Puritan ethic.

When I was younger, I had a piercing nostalgia for the medieval, saw it as a kind of historical bassinet or crib. But then I went to Gubbio, advertised in the guidebook as one of Italy's quintessential medieval towns. Foreboding, hardfaced, inhospitable, Gubbio reminds me now of my bathroom.

"Are we middle class or upper middle class?" my twelve-year-old son asks. I don't know how to answer him. My bathroom confuses the issue.

Looking at him, I wonder whether my soul is prematurely gray, whether I have grown impervious to adventure and am fit only for wallowing in sleek services and feverish reassurance, in an incubator like the famous B. F. Skinner box.

What does it all mean? Am I seeking, not comfort or convenience in my bathroom, but security? Am I afraid, first thing in the morning, to be thrown on my own devices?

What a cruel setting-up exercise: to have to show ingenuity, to effect an instant compromise between human frailty and refractory objects. No man is a pioneer in his bathroom, but travels the other way to regression.

In the powder room of a friend's house, I counted sixty-seven art objects. Coy pictures, cut glass, soap in the shape of fruit, a cornucopia, apothecary jars, multicolored glass balls in a ceramic bowl, cigar molds, huge, hand-hammered keys—a riot of metaphor, a water closet of witticisms gentled by art. I took heart; I resolved to decorate my bathroom.

But, alas, the wall space accommodates only a towel rack and a small medicine cabinet, which permits me a minimum of cosmetic refinement: comb, razor, toothbrush, deodorant, Band-Aids, nail scissors, eyewash.

The plumber pulls a long face, is discouraging. Fifteen hundred dollars in labor alone, not including tile, which he does not touch, or appliances. An honest working man, he is uncomfortable in my bathroom, tries to keep the pity out of his eyes. While his condescension is a credit to his manners, I know he will anatomize my bathroom over supper with his wife.

No champion of the modern, I long, all the same, for an up-to-the-minute, bank-reference bathroom where technology and sensuality embrace, where I can be steamed open like a love letter. Bathrooms plumb our depths. A triumphant new bath, by sympathetic magic, makes us new and triumphant, too.

I'm toying with an idea. Behind my house, I have a five-acre field that I don't really need. Suppose I were to sell it. I could find a good architect and tear out a few walls, and then there would be nothing to stop me from dwelling in marble halls.

As they say at Esalen, if you don't love yourself, who will?

Portrait of
a Moral Heroine

*E*veryone has a theory about her. She's rigid; she's frigid; she's compulsive. In place of a personality, she has a defense mechanism. She is the world's champion coper. She's a bore, a Renaissance woman, a saint, a peach.

Her name comes up at parties. Women who drink too much, who have affairs, or go to New York City to shop away their anxiety find her hard to take. Her mysterious happiness baffles even her friends. Hasn't she heard about the human condition?

She defies our categories and makes us uneasy. We prefer to believe we are all in the same boat, slightly seasick, heading for white water.

I like her, without knowing why. Perhaps if I try to describe her to you, I'll stumble on the answer.

While she is quite good-looking, she plays it down, for to be too attractive is to invite the world's attention and this is not her design. Her dark blond, unbleached hair is cut by a local man in a short, no-nonsense style, Except at parties, she wears only a dab of lipstick, nothing on her eyes. Her clothes are the practical sort of uniform of a woman who is forever climbing in or out of a car in order to make herself useful at a school or community service.

She tends toward slacks because she is a little ashamed of the tennis muscles in her legs. I've seen her play, and her tennis is methodical rather than inspired, because she is more concerned with being a good partner than with making brilliant shots. On the court, as everywhere, she is reliable.

At the beach, her two-piece bathing suit is as sexy as a sand castle. Yet her figure is fine, for all of her forty-odd years and two teen-age daughters. It is maintained, not by dance or exercise classes or by gardening and tennis, but by the isometric tension of keeping her balance.

When her face is in repose, she appears to be listening for something. I can't make up my mind whether it is a joyous sound she is waiting for—bird calls, church bells, children playing, the bark of a dog—or an alarm of some kind, the throb of her pulse perhaps.

When she talks to me, her eyes meet mine with such generic enthusiasm that she seems to look all around and through, rather than at me. Unlike the city woman's deliberately low voice, hers is high. She sings her convictions. Her conversation is confined to tangibles. She leans toward facts and is shy about speculation. It is impossible to lure her into an intimate statement about men or women. Her sense of privacy is like an electric burglar alarm. When we talk about books, her taste is sound, allowing for a prejudice against what she calls morbid. She prefers nonfiction, but has a soft spot for pastoral poetry.

While she is athletic, she does not move particularly well. In walking, she detours around her sexuality, and this same aura of modesty lends a mild clumsiness to her gestures.

Her husband is a decent fellow, a satisfactory partner in the business of life. He is good-looking, well made and gentlemanly. They do everything together—tennis, ski, sail, concerts and theater—as if they were concerned that neither of them should inadvertently enjoy life more than the other.

For me, the most remarkable thing about her is her closeness to nature. It is the one place where her animal self shows through. She looks at a garden as some women look at a lover, and when she sees land and sky skillfully composed, or sun on the water stretching away, her lips soften and curl and she moves as if she hears music. When this contact with nature fills her with a dangerous vivacity, she sprays her energy like a garden hose into efficient and selfless action.

It is my impression that, after two children and seventeen years of marriage, her sexuality centers on nurturing. I would guess that she is better at giving than receiving, that she sees herself as a means rather than an end. She has planted her daughters deep in life and they cannot help but bloom. I suspect that she supports her husband emotionally, rather like a trellis that spreads like a fan, but this is no reflection on him because it is difficult to see how any man in our time could develop a masculinity to meet her femininity.

In my conjecturing, she finds more satisfaction in her morality, her sense of being in place in the world, than in her conjugal bed. The pull of personal cohesion may be more profound than sexual pleasure. Her fidelity is famous throughout the community and men do not press her in proportion to her attractiveness. They can sense that, if she were to have an affair, which I see as an unthinkable thing, it would be like Jacob wrestling with the angel. I can hear her saying, "I will not let thee go except thou bless me."

Like so many other people who have moved from the city

to the country, I am always looking for structures, for images to supplant those I gave up. She is one of my images, a figure in the porch of a cathedral, a woman in front of a house in the country. She is my moral heroine, a twentieth-century translation of George Eliot. She helps me to see the logic of the landscape, like one of those figures in a classical painting who points out the scene to the others.

Job Snobs

A *man* came to pump out my septic tank and I was surprised to see that he was young, handsome, even elegant. Tall, slender, with a casual grace of movement, he might easily have passed for a marchese or an actor. His voice was melodious, his speech precise.

My wife, who saw him too, said, "He's not what you'd expect." And suddenly I thought, "Well, what would we expect in a man who pumps out our septic tank? What should he look like? A rat? A dung beetle? A devil with a forked tail?"

It occurred to me that my wife and I, like most of the people we know, are job snobs. We rate work in terms of its distance from reality. For our "class," the real is too humble. We tolerate it only on a chart or drawing board. We deal in Platonic essences.

We are the managers of our world. We manipulate symbols, wear white gloves of abstraction. Our work is remote, discreetly out of sight, an hour's train ride from our home. Some of us have children of ten or twelve who have never been to our offices, who could not accurately describe what we do.

Only on weekends, or on vacation, are we allowed to fondle the actual. In costume for the occasion, armed with expensive toys from the hardware store, we get out and putter, play at working with our hands. We boast and joke about our little manual jobs. When we have our early evening drink, we are filled with a special satisfaction, with the feeling of contact. Our fatigue is positively sensual.

We think of ourselves as running the show, but we rarely reflect that it is the mechanics of this world who keep it running. The sense of removal from mere things that used to be our pride has become a source of ambiguity and anxiety. Those of us who work in what is quaintly called communications have been wondering for some time just what it is that we have to communicate.

In the last decade, ecology has reintroduced us to the real, the tangible, the natural, and some of us secretly long to throw up abstraction and snuggle up in the arms of the concrete. A few still talk about retiring to a farm or opening an antiques shop.

There is a lurking feeling that things are breaking down and no one is willing to repair them. Our work seems to need not management or creativity, whatever that is, but maintenance. As Walker Percy said in a prophetic novel, when our civilization falls apart it will not be a result of politics, but because the mechanics have thrown down their tools.

Some of us have so little faith in our jobs that we can't pass along our values to our sons, who grow up feeling that they want to seize the world in their hands. Tinkering with their bikes or cars, their eyes are hard with competence. Adolescence is a dream of power, and in their secret hearts the young may see their fathers as living in a senile relation to the real.

I know a man, an executive in an office, who is profoundly upset because his son has dropped out of college to work as a garbage collector. His son just laughs and says, "I'm chairman of the board, tycoon of the organic. I'm closer to the truth than anyone you know."

He might also have said that most of us deal with garbage in one way or another. To be a doctor, for example, is the most vaunted of all professions. Yet what does a doctor do? Quite apart from stool and urine samples, he has to oppose the human body's persistent tendency to decline into a lump of exalted garbage.

A lawyer's work, too, often arises out of the deterioration, the trashing, of human relations. Legal language is the garbage dump of meaning and it is possible to see politics, particularly bureaucracy, as septic systems that are never pumped out.

Psychiatrists' offices are knee-deep in emotional garbage of the most intimate kind. Teachers vacillate between filling children's heads with garbage or trying to empty them of it. A literary critic, who is sometimes regarded as a secular priest, has to climb right into the can.

A copywriter in an advertising agency is certainly no stranger to garbage, nor is a salesman. Perhaps the great panjandrum of garbage is the television comic, who paddles in the waste materials of the culture as a child plays in a mud puddle.

Of course, there's a danger of going too far, of sentimentalizing manual labor, seeing it all as a Zen exercise or a therapeutic dance. Some of us have moved so far from the real that objects have assumed mystical qualities. There are people in craft shops who caress the palpable as if it was a love object. While the psychiatrist may behave like a patient in the presence of the mechanic who tunes his Porsche, it is an oversimplification to chant, "I make, therefore I am."

But while there's no need to romanticize them, we have no

business condescending to blue-collar workers. My plumber is wittier than some stockbrokers I know. My tree man has an easy natural dignity that a college president might envy. My handyman's manners are positively courtly and he knows more about the nature of things than Lucretius. If my neighbor across the street, who is a builder, were to run for President of the United States, I would sooner vote for him than at least one leading candidate I can think of.

The middle class needs to reexamine its categories. I think it would be a good idea if we called up the septic tank people, the garbage collector, the plumber, the handyman, the garage mechanic, and tried to get them to come over together. If they all pitched in as a team with the tools of their respective trades, they might be able to clear up the mess of our thinking.

The Last

Married Couple

in Connecticut

It's been raining in Connecticut and all our friends
are divorcing. We're worried, my wife and I. We don't want to
be sticks in the mud, the only married persons in the neighborhood. It's a troubling situation from many angles. Ecologi-
cally, for example, all these divorces could spell disaster. With
everyone pulling up roots, the whole area may wash away.

The husbands will leave, of course, and the wives stay
behind. With mixed feelings, I imagine a matriarchal society,
myself the only man. Will I be popular or a pariah, the target
of their bitterness? What will this do to our dinner parties? I
see an immensely long table lined with women, stretching
into the distance like a de Chirico vista.

How will they react to being alone, all these divorced
women? Will they roam the fields and roads in packs, or hide,
like gothic heroines, behind locked doors and drawn shades?
Perhaps they'll become androgynous, independent, a new
breed we won't know what to do with.

And the husbands who are fleeing to New York City, how
will they manage? Will they frequent massage parlors, lurk in

Central Park? I see them joining athletic clubs, sitting in the men's bar after fifty-seven games of squash, staring into their drinks with lost eyes.

Maybe, my wife says, we're being too pessimistic. She paints a more sanguine picture: the women learning belly dancing, studying semiotics at the New School, holding self-help clinics, enjoying their sisterhood.

The men will write novels, quit their suffocating careers, practice I Ching. They'll wrestle nude in their Greenwich Village studios like Gerald and Birkin in *Women in Love*, reaffirm their atavistic ties, their bonding instincts. They'll play volley ball in Washington Square to the beat of conga drums.

But the children, what about the children? At night, on the wind, we will hear the sound of their crying. I will be a big brother or foster father to fifty boys—do I have enough masculinity to go around? Not necessary, my wife says. Children are so plastic. They can adapt to anything. In a world where we are all alienated, what's one parent more or less?

Feeling that there is no longer any reason to be polite, that in fact it's gone out of style, we confront our friends who are divorcing. "What seems to be the matter?" Accusations burst out like abscesses, we are spattered with the symptomatology of marriage in the seventies.

"She refuses to develop a backhand." "He only likes to make love in the swimming pool." "She sneers at my driving." "He begins all his sentences with 'hopefully.'" "She won't quit shaving her armpits." "His hips are too wide." "She flirts with the dog." "He hates foreign films."

Their problems do not seem insurmountable, we suggest, but they disagree. They're divorcing. "Our evenings lack promise," a husband says, quoting a Donald Barthelme story.

"We doubled our loneliness by marrying," his wife says, quoting Jean Cocteau. "The heaviest object in the world is the body of the woman one has ceased to love," the husband says, quoting Vauvenargues. "Every man is an island entire in himself," his wife says, paraphrasing John Donne.

They moved out to Connecticut, these couples, to get away from the noise and dirt of the city and now they have discovered the noise and dirt of the self, so they are divorcing. They want to unlearn all the lessons, to be new again to someone.

"Will you still love us?" they ask. "Of course," we answer. "We will always love you, together or apart, now and forever."

At night, in bed, we talk about it, my wife and I. Can we really salvage them? We go over the couples, one by one. Marcus is so manic: Without Kate's silences to soak him up and soften his edges, he'll be like a dentist's drill. And if he isn't there, what will we say to her? Alison is as dependent as a newborn baby: unless Saul is at her side, she'll want to sit in our laps. And if he isn't fathering her, he'll start on us. Hilary has all the money: when she divorces Jules, she'll be too rich for us and he'll be too poor. Andrew and Liza are both so sexy: once they separate, nobody will be safe with either of them. In every case, the answer is the same: United they stand, divided they fall into the impossible category.

We look at each other, the last married couple in Connecticut, with wild surmise. The thing we have always dreaded and desired has finally come about. We are alone together.

Shifting the Weight

It would be hard for me to say, even now, why I went to Jack Wiener. My wife, who is a dancer, had spoken of him as someone who had changed her in some fundamental sense and several of her dancer friends described him in equally rapturous terms. He had not only changed and improved the way they moved, he had also altered the way they felt themselves to exist. I was interested in what they said, but only peripherally. Every art form has it peculiar shop talk.

Then one day as I was writing in my study, as I bent over the page with a pencil in my hand, I felt the weight of my self, the burden of my life, pressing, pressing on me. It seemed to affect the rhythm of my thoughts and the movement of my pencil on the page, and I felt, all at once, that I would like to shift that weight, to carry it differently. It came to me with the force of a melancholy revelation that I had borne myself in an unconscious, unchanging manner all through my history, and that perhaps this was a foolish and unnecessary thing to do. I felt as if I had already posed for my statue, taken up my stance once and for all, and that I would never make a startling or surprising gesture as long as I lived.

"What kind of gesture?" I asked myself. "What do you mean?" When I tried to define this new feeling, the best I could do was to fall back on the title of a poem by an author I admire: "Movements of the Internal Being." The poem begins: "The powder magazine of the internal being is not always exploding. You might suppose it was sand."

I don't have a mystical turn of mind and I distrust things that can't be described. I searched myself, felt myself all over, and I could find nothing but a kind of nostalgia, a premonition of reduced opportunities. Perhaps, I thought, I am dying, entering upon the long process of gradually growing still. I don't know. I do know that there have been mornings when I opened my eyes and thought that I would like to enter the day by doing a soft-shoe dance. My feet whispering on the floor, I would recapitulate, step-by-step, my entire life, all its joys and sorrows, including my continuing relations with my deceased mother and father.

I was afraid that my body had ceased to be my best friend, had become instead an innocent bystander, even a victim. I began to exercise systematically. I ran four miles a day without ever feeling that I was overtaking myself. I played at games which imposed rules on my anxiety. After showering, I looked at myself in the full-length mirror in the bathroom. While I had not changed, I appeared different to myself.

Wasn't it true that bodies used to say more, used to sing? Look at the Apollo Belvedere, the Romanesque sculptures, the descents from the Cross. I remembered Michelangelo's David, and Adam reaching for the hand of God. I wanted to stand poised, like the Angels of the Annunciation. What were de Kooning's women but bodies furious with neglect? Why were we mocked by models in fashion magazines?

Gestalt psychologists believe that thoughts distribute themselves as shapes in our bodies. Where are these shapes?

The muffled voice of my body kept me awake at night.

I have heard that amputees feel pain in the missing part. What if all the parts are missing?

And so I found myself at The School for Creative Movement in the Arts, facing Jack Wiener in my bare feet, blue jeans and a specially purchased sleeveless undershirt.

"What is it you want?" Jack asked. "Why have you come to me?" He is a handsome man in his forties who looks like a dancer on vacation.

"I don't know," I said. "I came here to find out why I wanted to come here."

"It doesn't matter," Jack said. "Let's begin as if we knew. We will start with the beat, which is the basis of everything. Man is an animal with a pulse." He put on an early blues record. "I'd like to see you walk around to the beat."

I walked. The beat was strong, comfortable, homely, familiar.

"Now breathe in time to your walking. Try to walk and breathe to the beat."

It was a natural sensation, the simple satisfaction of things falling into place.

"Sometimes," Jack said, "people move against instead of with their breathing, and this is what happens." He did a bit of a Broadway routine, first dancing against his breathing, then with it. I could see the difference. One flowed with the music and the other sawed across it.

"Let's see how you move," Jack said. He put on a rock record.

"Move?" I was suddenly timid. "Move how?"

"However you like. Walk around to the beat until you feel that you are breathing with it. When you are ready, just talk back to the music."

Walking around again, I swallowed and digested the beat until I could feel it squirming inside me. I like to dance and I go to discothèques with my wife, yet I was self-conscious all the same. I did a few standard steps and then broke into free-form variations. I usually dance as if I considered it a form of parody, though I could not say what I think I'm parodying, or why.

Jack switched to a jazz record and I played around with that. I began to feel at home with him, to look upon him as a father.

The next week we reviewed the first session and then Jack put on a James Brown record. I find it easy to respond to James Brown and I was also finding it progressively easier to accept Jack's presence. I behaved as if I were dancing at a party among friends. Most of my friends regard me as a surprisingly spontaneous dancer, but they would be less surprised if I confessed to them that I know my spontaneity by heart.

"Shall I give you my impressions?" Jack said after a while. He waited until I nodded yes. "You appear to feel secure in this beat, in the structure of a strong and simple rhythm. To put it another way, you don't seem to be anxious in a finite situation of this sort."

He paused and smiled. "I'm tempted to say that you condescend to the music. You assume the attitude of an amused tourist, someone from a superior culture. Your response is ironical, ambivalent, distanced. You are very much on top of what you're doing."

He did a brief imitation of my dancing, made it look almost disdainful. "Your style is very staccato, very macho, like flamenco, fighting, sex. I see humor, but little affection or confiding."

I could think of nothing to say. It is both thrilling and threatening to be laid bare.

"Today I want you to be aware of the possibilities, of the vocabulary of the body, which is richer than most people suppose. You have a head, a neck, shoulders, a chest, abdomen, pelvis, hips, thighs, knees, legs, ankles, toes." Jack moved each part as he named it. "You have fingers, hands, wrists, forearms, elbows, upper arms. You are an intricacy of moveable parts and I would like to see you try to bring them all into play. Think of yourself as a rich man, indulging his every whim."

He put on a jazz record and I hesitated, lost in the rubble of my parts. Jack made a few moves to encourage me and I realized that he could illustrate anything.

I tried, but I had never felt such a man of parts before, and I made a mess of it.

"That's all right," Jack said. "Take your time."

I started again. I was a baby counting his toes. For the rest of the session, I introduced myself to myself.

The following week, Jack began with a fast African rumba—drums, sticks and gourds. I'm very fond of African drumming. It usually has a third or even fourth beat in addition to the standard one or two. I chose a sharp-toned drum that was playing on the offbeat and moved to that.

"Good," Jack said. "Very good. If you lived in Africa, you might find happiness there."

"Yes, but I don't live in Africa."

"And that's why you're here?"

"I'm here because I'm not somewhere else, because one day at my desk, when I wasn't moving at all, I got the crazy feeling that I don't want to move in the same way for the rest of my life. I don't want to be a signature on a document. I hate the idea of being predictable."

Jack waited to see whether I had anything more to add. Then he said, "Shall I point something out?" He always asked permission before walking into my personality. "You almost always retract your movements after you have extended them. You tuck them back, as if you wanted to return home after each venture."

He was right, of course. I prefer not to sleep at other people's houses, even though, under certain circumstances, it is more interesting.

"Perhaps you might try," Jack said, "to travel in a continuous line, away from your starting point."

I cheated. I strung together a series of discrete movements, like wash on a line.

"Look at all this space," Jack said, extending his arms. "It's yours. You paid for it."

At our next meeting, Jack said, "you learn quickly. I think you may be ready to ask yourself why you called me up, why you are standing here in your bare feet. Unless you ask the question, you may never know the answer."

"Isn't a profound question almost as good as an answer?"

Jack thought about this. "Perhaps. But only if you keep posing the question." He walked over to the phonograph and put on a record. It was a Chopin nocturne.

When he saw the expression on my face, he laughed. "I'm curious to see—and you may be too—what happens when you take yourself by surprise, when you have nothing to fall back on and can only go forward."

I listened to the Chopin. "What do you expect me to do to that?"

"I expect you to do the unexpected."

"I'm not a professional dancer. I wouldn't know where to start."

"Start there, with not knowing."

I didn't move.

"Are you afraid to be awkward? Awkwardness is the beginning of everything. You can even make a style of awkwardness, if you like."

I remembered something Theodor Reik had said. In forty years of analyzing people, he had discovered that men were often terrified of tenderness. I realized that I was terrified of Chopin. Bach is my kind of composer. His emotions are so cosmic, so far beyond my reach, that I feel safe with him.

"Walk around," Jack suggested. "Feel the beat. Breathe."

I walked and tried to ingest Chopin. "Soft," Jack said. "Serpentine. Vulnerable. Androgynous. Feel your way into it like a blind man."

"Show me," I said. "Give me an idea."

Jack made a few simple gestures. They seemed both appropriate and natural. With a great sigh, I plucked up my courage and did a bad imitation of what Jack had just done. I was like a child being toilet-trained. I halted. I felt terribly sorry for myself. I tried to think, but it was not a matter for thinking.

I extended one arm. I did a half-turn, raised my head, lowered it to my chest. I bent my knees and was about to straighten them when I froze.

I felt my full weight upon me. It was heavy, so heavy. I wanted to shift it, but I didn't know how. Something like an immense sneeze gathered in my chest.

I stood there with my knees bent, utterly still, until Jack said, "'Good."

I straightened up. I began to breathe again. "What was good about it?"

"You tried. You permitted yourself to act without knowing."

"I made a fool of myself."

"No," Jack said. "If you work hard, that will come in time."
We left it there until next week.

The Poorest Man
in Fairfield

Y*ears ago*, I asked a fraud whose father I had never met what kind of man he was. My friend thought for a moment and said: "He's the kind of man who, when he walks in the street, always keeps his eyes on the ground, looking for money."

I laughed, but now, as the poorest man in Fairfield, I wonder. Sitting in his house, talking to another friend, one who has never known what it is to need money, I'm thinking about the difference between him and me, about the physiognomy of need.

The presence of my friend, this particular man, is slightly unsettling. It is not his fault, but when I'm with him I feel as if I, too, looked for money on the ground, or in the air, anywhere. It seems to me that I must have on my face a questing, interrogative expression, that I am like a man who is listening for an announcement of some sort, something as yet unspecified, a message from fate. I am reminded of the crows in the sky in Van Gogh's ominous painting of wheat fields.

I imagine a pornography of need, an embarrassing gleam in my eye, an unbecoming absorption in an indispensable process, rather like the absorption of a man who eats without raising his eyes from his plate. Is there a telltale line, a money line, around my mouth, eyes and forehead?

You can almost hear the need for money, like a noise in the psyche, like the engine of a cheap car, like the peculiarly querulous sound of conversation in an inexpensive place. A man who doesn't have enough money spills his hunger into his speech, bites off his consonants, uses too many words with connotations of compulsion.

I study my friend. I like him, even admire him. Though we are separated by need, I wish I could borrow his manner, as I once borrowed his 450 SL when my Ford was being fixed.

How innocent his face is, how boyish. His eyes gaze out on a child's garden of verses. He sees life not as a drama, but a series of anecdotes. He has bought off necessity, he owns improvisation. His face has the calm of a man after love-making.

Not far from here, he has a boat. It is an appropriate symbol, this boat, a boy's toy and a man's independence. The boat moves effortlessly, lives on air. The wheel in his hand, my friend gazes out over charted seas. He smiles, a smile without a twist in it, no hint of a grimace.

Once I said to him: "I wish I had lived in one place as long as you have. Your mortgage must be almost paid off by now."

And he said: "Oh I don't have a mortgage. My father warned me against them."

Many times I have asked myself, did he say this with irony? I doubt it. He doesn't use irony. Though it costs more than necessity, I believe he has bought off irony too. Why should he fuss with shades of meaning when he lives in the sun?

I admit it, I feel elevated in his company, I rise up out of myself. We become gentlemen together, he and I. Sometimes it has comical consequences. There was an evening when we were talking to another man at his house. As an incidental detail, the other man mentioned an end table that had cost his wife $22,000.

The story he was telling required the detail and he implicitly apologized for it. Later, it developed that this other man had written a book and wanted to get a sophisticated opinion regarding it. I didn't tell him that people like me get substantial fees for this kind of work. I took the book home and did it for nothing, because we were all gentlemen together.

My friend has old money, as opposed to new money, and the difference is important. New money, which you don't inherit, but make yourself, has a momentum built into it. It tends to become an addiction. You feel that you must go on making and spending it.

I remember a new-money man who complained to me that he was bored to death with his business and would give anything to retire. I pointed out that he must have been worth at least a million dollars. This was fifteen years ago when a million dollars still meant something. He could certainly retire, if he wished, on a million dollars.

His answer was significant. "I've grown used to a certain way of life," he said, "and I can't cut back even $5 a week."

Easy circumstances, man of substance, independent means, a competence: what pleasant expressions these are. And what a pleasant expression my friend wears as he talks without undue emphasis in his well-modulated voice. The lines in his face come from laughing, from looking into the sun.

Would I change places? How much is my kind of consciousness worth to me? What would I take for my tragic sense of life? What would hold me together if not necessity?

A divorced woman told me that she never would have married her husband if she had known how much money he was going to inherit. "I've seen too many men drown in money," she said. But my friend doesn't drown in his money. He's a good sailor who glides smoothly over the surface of it.

I could never live as gracefully as he does. They say that the devil finds mischief for idle hands, but I believe that my friend is in the keeping of the Holy Ghost. For my part, I need my purgatory. It is only by the light of the fires that I can see.

Need is the last adventure. There are no others. For me, at least, need is tension. When I get paid each month, I feel like a quarterback sizing up his receivers. It's all in the game. Why, if I could free my mind from money, could give it to any one thing, I might blow my fuse.

It's terrible, but need colors everything. I'm thinking of my single touchstone of purity, my love for my children. I believe that I prize them so desperately partly because I bought and paid for them. As long as I'm alive, the account can never be closed, and this is my one heroism.

My friend gets up to fill my glass. We are drinking champagne because his son finished off the beer. We've been playing squash at the club and feel like something cold.

I'd rather have beer, but I don't mind champagne. It's the quality of your thirst, not what you drink, that counts.

Free Associating

in the Attic

I'm cleaning out our attic, throwing out old useless things to make way for new useless things. The shuffle, veer, tack and jib of taste call for constant revision, remorseless relegations. That piece we bought and showed with so much pride first grew doubtful, then downright wrong. We've fallen out of love again: up to the attic with it.

A person whose attic is full is like someone with sinusitis. I had it once and went to the doctor to have my hollows drained. A painful business, but afterward you are lighter than air, defy the law of gravity, your voice rings like a bell.

Our bulging attic haunts me, makes our house so top-heavy I'm afraid it will fall over, spill our second thoughts all through the neighborhood, expose the dregs, lees, silt and sediment, the bones, fossils and fragments of our history.

Living in the country encourages hoarding. We are far enough apart for secrets, for eccentricity. Our fields were once a farm, devoted to husbandry. Now we husband our past in the common grave of our attic. Choosing a house with an attic is like buying a child's clothes a size too large, as my family did when I was small. It leaves room to grow.

Modern houses have no attics. What do they need them for? A modern person gathers no moss. He dissolves his history, his errors, into theories which he displays in bookshelves in his living room. City people, too, live without attics. They give their moltings, their waste products, to the Salvation Army or the sanitation department.

It smells of mothballs up here in my attic, an old-fashioned smell like Bay Rum or the talcum powder women used to wear. Do people still use mothballs? Is anything made of wool anymore?

What is that, bruising my shins? A piece of furniture? It looks like one, it's made of wood, old wood. I puzzle over possible functions. The thing is large enough to sit on, yet it is not designed for sitting. Nor can it be a table. I see no broken ends, no missing parts: It is complete. A complete mystery.

Here's our luggage, vain with foreign labels. Before the children were born, we used to go to Europe every summer to mitigate our rampant Americanism. My wife gave me this enormous suitcase, with a card saying that we were going to have an adventurous life. When it was packed, the suitcase was so heavy I couldn't lift it. A life of adventure is a weighty proposition.

Rooting around in a corner, I straighten up too quickly, and impale myself on the nails in the roof. For some reason I have never understood, the shingles in old houses are always put on with very long nails. They look like barracuda teeth, and in fact, attics can bite you if you're not careful.

I see a pair of crutches, from the time I broke my leg. Do I expect to break it again? There's a gun in the corner, a present from my brother-in-law, who is a collector. Shall I shoot someone? Myself? What are we doing with a brass birdcage? We never had a bird.

The floor is gritty in our attic. Are these squirrel or bat droppings, or just the rotting of our yesterdays? These things we hoard up here like squirrels, will they tide us over the winter of our discontent? Are we discontented? If we are, can we store it in the attic?

Rummaging in another box, I discover that it contains white sheets. Nothing but white sheets and pillow cases, dozens of them. As far as my unpracticed eye can judge, they are not worn out. On the contrary, some of them are nearly new. I can only surmise that we cannot repose on white sheets anymore. Our sleep, our sex, must be more colorful.

Thousands of letters—what should I do with those? I'm not prepared to go through them again, it would be worse than psychoanalysis. I read somewhere that Balzac wrote enough letters to the woman he eventually married to stuff a mattress. Perhaps I should stuff a mattress with these and let them whisper to me in the night.

A small, rather battered box, carefully sealed up. I know that one. It holds my father's ashes in an urn. I've had it for twenty years, while I tried to settle on a ceremony that would satisfy our peculiar affection.

Photographs, a large carton of photographs, loose and in albums. I will not succumb to the albums, which, I know, will take me back, like senility, to a time when everyone was a child. I pick up an armload of girls I knew when I was a bachelor, riffle through them, musing over the wild rise and fall of enthusiasm I felt for each and every one. It was like jumping into the air simply because I had so much spring in my legs, then coming down again. Did I ever manage to love any of them? Can anyone under thirty love?

One of these girls was a model. Her photograph is large, professional, her shoulders are bare and she rests her chin on one and smiles at me with the up-and-under look. Do girls still smile that way? The others, too, are wearing obsolete expressions. They look innocent, expectant, optimistic, eager to please. They are like apprentices in the business of living, unconscious of themselves except as members of a species, or a team. That insistence on the sense of self, of stubborn singularity, which is the cosmetic of contemporary women, seems altogether absent.

It is true of my wife's picture, too, as I study her before she became a wife. How open and candid her face is, framed in short hair and faith. She is what my friends and I used to call Pure Food and Drug Act stuff. She gazes out into the future as if she asked nothing better than to agree with me, to help me in some sweet, strenuous pursuit. Lingering over the photograph, I realize that I thought she'd stay this way, and I would never have to do more than love and amuse her. How is it, I wonder, that neither of us has stashed the other up here?

This will never do. I'm not getting on with the job. I haven't found a single thing to throw out. Perhaps I never will, perhaps I'll just keep piling more things up in geological layers, right to the ceiling.

I have a friend, a Gestalt therapist who is writing a book in which he says that most people suffer from one of two fears: abandonment or engulfment. I think that, if I could choose, I would prefer to be engulfed. And so I'll trust to my attic. One of these days, when it and I have had about as much as we can take, the door will fly open and the past will tumble down the stairs to rejoin me.

The Ontology

of Boots

When *I* need intellectual stimulation on a weekday afternoon, I wheel out my gearless bicycle and make my way with unamplified torque to my son's school. My experiences there comprise a curriculum of such depth and variety that I owe it to the community to set them down. Here, then, is a record of my most recent visit, which began with an inquiry into the ontology of boots and shoes.

"But they're not boots," I said. "They're shoes, the same kind of shoes he has been wearing for the past six years." My son had been censured for wearing boots, which are banned by the school's sartorial code.

"The drawing of distinctions," the headmaster said, "is the sacred duty of schools. While there are some gray areas, the differential factors in this instance can nevertheless be sustained with confidence.

"Boot derives from the Middle English *bote*, which in turn stems from the same root as the French *bot*, as in *pied bot*, or club foot. *Bot*, as you will recall, means toad or squat creature; i.e., a boot is a squat creature. Shoe is quite another matter, descending from the Old High German *scura,* a barn, that is to say a housing for the foot, or the Latin *scutum,* a shield. The Sanskrit *kosa,* a container or case, is certainly relevant."

"I concede the fact," I said, "that they are sturdy shoes, warm shoes, water-repellent shoes, but these are not the exclusive properties of boots."

"Boots," the headmaster said, "carry a pejorative connotation, which we here at the school try to avoid. 'Trouble deaf heaven with my bootless cries,' as Shakespeare put it, bootless being synonymous with feckless. Bootleg makes no bones about its illicit nature, and Fascist Italy, as you know, was stigmatized as Mussolini's boot . . ."

"I've just paid $45 for these shoes which you have interdicted as boots."

"The issue transcends boots and shoes," the headmaster said, picking up a beer can from the beautifully kept lawn and putting it in his pocket. "They are merely symbols, as Van Gogh intuited when he painted his own shoes. He saw them as objective correlatives of the quidditas, the whatness, of life itself.

"The distinction we have been discussing goes to the very heart, the liver and lights of education. How many great scholars have devoted their lives to the making of distinctions. When St. Augustine said of God, 'Do not presume to call him ineffable, for that is to say too much about him,' he read us a lesson beside which boots and shoes pale into insignificance.

"Even your secular scholars," the headmaster continued, warming to his theme, "even your secular giants were religious about distinctions. You are no doubt familiar with the fact that Rabelais's Pantagruel devoted his doctoral dissertation to the nice distinctions between various forms of, well—shall we say lavatory appurtenances."

"Yes, of course," I said. "How could I forget? Well, I must be off. I'm one of the judges in a public-speaking contest."

As a book critic for a newspaper, I am sometimes asked to lend my expertise to the school. I have lectured the upper forms, with some success, on such variegated themes as the composition of thank-you notes, the dangling modifier in Restoration drama, and the glottal stop as a function of ineffectual rage.

Generally I share the judging chores with two women. While it is never the same two women, all of them seem to have something in common. After telling me how ardently they follow my recommendations in the newspaper, they invariably vote against me. I have yet to see one of my candidates win, and today was no exception. While I voted for "The Hitchhiker as Picaresque Hero," the prize went to "The Pathos of Being Left-handed in a Right-handed World."

Feeling a bit disconsolate, I went over to the playing fields, where the battle of Wall Street is to be won, and watched the soccer game. Although my son is on the team, I suffer from a constitutional inability to understand soccer. Mine was a handy generation, while soccer belongs to a footloose era. It always reminds me of a movie I saw when I was a child, in which Lon Chaney played an armless wonder in a circus.

There was a nosegay of pretty mothers, frisking like wood nymphs on the sidelines. Several of them have served as cheerleaders in their own school days and it is a lovely sight to see them doing handsprings and sexy little routines to urge on the fruit of their loins. Ordinarily rather reserved, they think nothing of crying "Fie!" and "Pshaw!" when the call goes against the home team.

The boys themselves are silent, in keeping with the classic tenet that athletes do not talk. While this lends them an air of precocious dignity, it is also true that several of the boys have succumbed to aphasia.

After the game, in an attempt to master my own emotions, not so much with respect to the boys as to the mothers, I took a pensive stroll around the grounds. The school is a huge nineteenth-century mansion, built in the English country style by a tycoon whose descendants still inhabit the second floor. Threading my way through the maze, which is the only means of access to the formal gardens and where seventeen boys have disappeared to date, I skirted the grotto and perched on the marble steps of the folly. If I had known the benefits of a school like this one, I reflected, what might I not have done? I felt the genius of the place like damp in my bones.

The setting sun bathed the statuary in the garden in a deep effulgence, as if their hearts were bleeding. I mounted my bicycle and pedaled slowly toward the parents' meeting. I dreaded the responsibility they had asked me to assume. There had been rumors to the effect that a fledgling instructor of English was exerting an unwholesome influence on the boys and I had been called in to assess the gravity of these allegations. One cannot be too careful about boys in private schools. Already, they are regarded as suspect by public school boys owing to their invariable habit of embracing one another in hand-to-hand combat.

There were more than twenty parents at the meeting, and their faces were grim. The occasion was so seriously regarded that martinis were served. I was surprised to see among those present an almost equal number of fathers and mothers.

"What exactly has this young man done?" I asked.

Everyone spoke at once. In the ensuing confusion, I could make out only the word poems.

"Poems?" I said. "What's this about poems?"

"He's got them writing poems," a mother said, stamping her $300 Chelsea Cobbler boot, which had, so far, not been interdicted.

"Poems!" I said. "By golly, this *is* serious!" I clasped my hands behind my back and teetered on my heels. "How long has this been going on?"

"I understand," another mother said, "that the instructor in question is in the habit of writing poems himself."

"It's a clear case of enthusiasm," I announced, "which used to be punished as a heresy. Something will have to be done, and soon. I have known a poet or two—in a purely professional way, of course—and I would hate to tell you the sort of lives they lead."

"What do you suggest?" a father grated. "I'll wring his poetic neck if you say the word."

"No, no, it need not come to that. Just give me a moment to think." Somebody thrust a fresh martini in my hand, and the answer came to me as if it had been in the glass.

"Work them," I said. "Work them 'til they drop. Yard chores, chopping wood, raking leaves, mending walls, cleaning out the attic and basement. As Thoreau said, 'A poet is someone who, having nothing to do, finds something to do.' So wear them out. And cold baths. Make them take cold baths."

The Body as Debris

O_n *South Beach* in Martha's Vineyard, the tide deposits stones, shells, seaweed, wood, cork and a few white plastic bottles. Sometimes it breaks down the restraining dunes that keep the water from flooding the land.

There is another tide, too, that deposits its debris on the beach and breaks down restraints. This is the tide of history or manners, and it strews some parts of the beach with human bodies.

When I walk or run up the beach, these bodies greet me in a literal confrontation. How very naked the naked truth is. The day writhes with revelations, as a poet said. I am struck by the extraneousness, the radical irrelevance, of undesired intimacy. I feel something like the sadness one is said to experience after love making, but in this case it doesn't follow lovemaking. It doesn't follow anything.

Love, or the absence of love, may be the heart of the matter, for we generally associate nakedness with that sentiment. The body of someone we love is not altogether naked, but clothed and framed in our feelings. We see it not simply as a body, but a symbol, a sacred text, an exclusive gift, a set of complex physical and metaphysical signals. More than anything else, it is the emotion we bring to it that makes a body beautiful.

In his book *The Nude*, Sir Kenneth Clark describes the impact of a body seen without the softening influence of feeling. "It is widely supposed," he writes, "that the naked human body is itself an object upon which the human eye dwells with pleasure and which we are glad to see depicted. But anyone who has frequented art schools and seen the shapeless, pitiful model that the students are industriously drawing will know that this is an illusion. The body is not one of those objects which can be made into art by direct transcription, like a tiger or a snowy landscape . . . A mass of naked figures does not move us to empathy, but to disillusion and dismay. . . . By long habit, we do not judge the body as a living organism, but as a design . . ."

When we see the body of someone we love, we have designs on it, we impose design. But when we look objectively at the figure of a stranger, it is doubly naked, stripped of both clothing and emotional associations, and we are likely to feel the force of Sartre's remark about the obscenity of flesh "that cannot be justified by the situation."

Most of the people who appear naked on South Beach would say that they are being free, honest or natural. I wonder about the naturalness. Some of these bodies blink and wince in the sun, like the unfocused eyes of a person who has taken off his glasses. The vaunted honesty of the age often has a sadomasochistic component. Here on the beach, it may suggest the person who shows you the scars of his operation, an operation that begins with birth and ends with death.

I'm not persuaded that these naked people are free, either,

for it's a much-debated question whether self-consciousness has not enslaved our bodies. Rembrandt painted a woman with the mark of a garter on her thigh, and it may be that bodies today bear the constricting marks of civilization. I suspect, too, that at least some of the nakedness on the beach is less an assertion of physical or emotional freedom than a political demonstration. It may also be an aspect of the current insistence on visible or palpable identity.

In a sense, these naked people are tourists of the physical. Fired with ecological enthusiasm, they have come to Martha's Vineyard to offer themselves to nature, to undress a balance that needs to be redressed. Unconsciously fearing that they are an endangered species, they advertise for sympathy.

I have an economic as well as an aesthetic objection to public nakedness. Our personalities, our very souls, have been so overexposed in this age of therapy that I think we need to keep something in reserve for those precious occasions when we wish to surprise one another. Part of the pleasure in the gift of the self lies in the unwrapping. Nakedness should be a drama for an audience of one, for there is nothing more wonderful than the wild surmise that attends the first disrobing.

Judging from the story a friend told me, the absence of this important ceremony has a curious effect. A man in his late twenties, my friend came up from New York City to spend a month on the Vineyard, where he struck up an acquaintance with a naked young woman on the beach. Eventually they became lovers, but while he was fond of her, he confessed that he suffered from what he called an amnesiac feeling in the relationship, as if, he said, he had skipped the first chapter in reading a book.

There are people of liberal persuasion who would argue that, if I don't enjoy the sight of naked bodies on the beach, I ought to ignore them. But do we want to learn to ignore the human body, to dismiss it as just one more white plastic bottle on the beach?

Responding to it positively could be just as problematical. Suppose that by some miracle one found all the bodies on South Beach attractive and reacted accordingly. Where would that lead? Sandor Ferenczi, a pupil of Freud's, wrote an extraordinary article about a small boy who fell into a coma at the sight of his mother's nakedness, which he had never seen before. According to Ferenczi, his mother's body was such a powerful stimulus that it short-circuited the boy's libido.

While a mature libido can usually cope with the sight of a naked body, two or three hundred may be sufficient to send it into mild shock. This would help to explain the odd absence of physical desire on seeing so many bodies. We may even be preparing ourselves for an all-embracing interpersonal coma.

Sir Kenneth Clark distinguishes three different moods of the body: energy, ecstasy and pathos. I'm afraid that, for me, on South Beach, pathos dominates. Most of us are not as lovely as we would like to be. After denying the animal in us for so many years, we have ceased to belong to any kingdom. We are the pariahs of evolution.

In earlier centuries, hanged men were sometimes left suspended on the gibbet as a reminder to the rest of the population, as a stimulus to melancholy reflection. This, I'm sorry to say, is how a good many of these naked bodies under the sun affect me. They bend my thoughts to mortality, to the sins of sloth and greed, to the cruelty of time and the proneness to corruption of the flesh. They are heraldic images of human suffering. It is as if modern painters had depicted a new age of martyrs, and they had marched out onto the beach.

Can I walk up to these naked people and say that this is not the lesson one wishes to read here? Shall I point out that I am on vacation? Do they know that they are violating my civil right to my own private form of innocence?

There Are No Grandmas Anymore

*T*here are no grandmas anymore. You won't find them in the kitchen, demonstrating the inscrutable wisdom of the stove. Your children aren't wearing sweaters, scarves or mittens knit by their indefatigable fingers. Grandma's mystical maternity, mellowed in wood, time or tradition, is no longer a family heritage.

Once curators of continuity in a discontinuous world, grandmas have deserted their posts. Small hands can no longer cling to their skirts, seeking a buffer zone between the fairy tale and the fierce world outside the front door. They can't, because grandmother is wearing slacks.

There are no more grandmas, just grandmothers—young, smart-looking, cigarette-smoking, cocktail-drinking, divorcing, athletic, theater-going women of a certain age, cool and composed at the wheels of their cars.

Of course, I'm talking about the middle class in the country. The working class still has grandmas. It's just another of their many advantages, like having more money than we do and wearing blue shirts that don't give them a rash like our turtlenecks.

We've lost grandma to Saks, Bergdorf's and Bendel's, to the beauty parlor and the health club. Instead of a rocking chair, she has an exercise bicycle, or she jogs. I see one grandmother jogging past my house every morning in a different outfit, her elegant tweed trousers snug on her neat hips. She is a mean tennis player, this grandmother, a challenging skier, and a formidable flirt. In spite of Shakespeare's "For you and I are past our dancing days," she is no slouch in a discothèque either.

"How earthy old people become," Thoreau said. "They remind me of mole crickets." I'd like to see him find a mole cricket in my neighborhood. Earthy, yes—but not in the sense he means. At one time, grandmas were beyond sexual competition and they offered a quiet emotional backwater for everyone. As plants bring oxygen into the air, grandmas exuded serenity, softened the sexual acoustics of the home, where the teenagers were on one passionate threshold and the parents on another.

Now grandmother's hat is back in the ring and the sexual static is loud in the living room. She who was an emotional midwife, a mother earth, has metamorphosed into a thrilling "older woman"—and who can blame her but the two generations of her selfish, abandoned babies?

A grandma used to be a mulch pile of memory, an unsolicited testimonial to the American past, a family album, a soothsayer, a link in the great chain of being. In William Faulkner's words, she had "prevailed."

Now she stops time, like a science-fiction movie. If she won't grow old, none of us can move on. Adults will remain children and children infants. In America today, it takes about sixty years to become an adult.

You can see that the girls miss her. Why else would they

have started wearing granny glasses and dresses? Some of them are already so haggard at twenty that they look as if they'd like to skip parenthood altogether—the dirty work— and go directly into the business of being grandmothers.

Life without grandmas is like living in California, where there are no seasons. I especially miss that autumnal quality that grandmas used to have. Whey it's not even safe to kiss them anymore. They've been to Esalen, or its equivalent, and you might get more than you bargained for. If you try to cry in their arms, who knows what you might stir up?

We've had to say goodbye to grandma as a baby-sitter because we're afraid to leave the children with her. Anyway she is usually out on a date and now it is we who have to sit up and wait for her, carefully scrutinizing her clothes as she comes in with a secret smile from her friend's car.

Nobody complains anymore about grandmother being underfoot, because she is usually off to Jakarta or Portugal. When she is at home, we sometimes try to chat with her, to reap the ripe fruit of her experience, but she insists on talking about the latest books, which we haven't read, or the new plays we haven't seen. When we reminisce, around the fireplace, about the past, she calls us morbid and urges us to get into what she terms "the here and now." A number of young mothers threw their backs out trying to do grandma's yoga exercises. I asked my eleven-year-old daughter what she wanted to be when she grew up and she said a grandmother.

There are no more grandmas—only guests, slim, sleek, creatures who move in mysterious ways. But I know what I'm going to do: I'm going to throw away my turtleneck sweaters and buy some blue shirts. Then I'm going to put an ad in the local paper:

Wanted: One grandma. Salary negotiable. Must have gray hair, capacious bosom, mustache. Housedress, slippers, shawl supplied.

Complimenting

Women

"*Shall I* compare thee to a summer's day?" You "walk in beauty, like the night." "Thy eyes are the betrayal/of bells comprehended through incense. . . . "

They won't do. It is getting harder to compliment women. They're tired of empty words, of being compared to flowers, landscapes, climates and other irrelevancies. They've changed, and the descriptions of them will have to change.

The truly contemporary woman recognizes the fact that many compliments are merely condescensions in disguise. Some are even a form of symbolic rape. When you praise a women for her "vital statistics"—her bust, waist and hip measurements—she doesn't have to be a feminist to find that depersonalizing.

An intelligent woman knows that the word beautiful generally refers to a set of physical prejudices, conditioned reflexes or statistics. There's been too much fuss about beauty anyway, as if it was a woman's principal function in life to be beautiful in order to please or excite a man. The whole business of beauty begs the question of character, personality, intelligence and talent—popularly known as "identity." It also fails to do justice to the unanalyzable idiosyncrasy of individual attraction.

Then what is a man to do? I, for one, find a deep satisfaction in complimenting a woman. That it may even be an innate need is suggested by the courting behavior of many birds and animals. In the presence of an agreeable woman, I feel a spontaneous joy, an impulse to make an unobscene noise, to celebrate her and share a warm and profoundly human moment. I would like to say to such a woman, "I'm glad you exist," but that's a bit general. I'd prefer to bring the compliment in closer to her, a little like an embrace.

I'm not sure why, but most compliments focus on the physical. Often the physical implies the metaphysical, especially the face. We do choose or shape ourselves to a degree. Also, one has to know a woman very well to venture a non-physical compliment without seeming presumptuous. Women are evolving so fast and so furiously that we see them as if by a strobe light. They don't stand still long enough for a spiritual compliment to catch up with them.

The solution, as I see it, is to frame more fundamental or radical compliments, to make our praise so permanently apt that no woman, however volatile, will ever outgrow it. I would like to try, also, to find a form of expression that, without being sexist, still does justice to that unique tension between the sexes, that hum or buzz that is neither exclusively physical nor metaphysical.

The thrill is gone, some say, but I don't believe it. You just have to look harder, sharper, deeper to locate it. I think of the new relationship between men and women as somehow athletic, spiritually athletic perhaps, and so I have been doing some calisthenics to get myself in shape for it. I rummaged through the literature on my shelves and in my head in order to condition my vocabulary and my conceptions. And in the process, I made a most serendipitous discovery. I found what I think is probably the most comprehensive compliment ever uttered by a man to a woman, one that is positively cosmic, yet intensely personal.

It occurs in *The Magic Mountain*, by Thomas Mann, and I'll have to tell you just a bit of the background of the novel before we get to this passage that gives me goose pimples every time I read it. Hans Castorp, the hero of the book, is a young German engineer who is visiting his cousin in a sanitarium for tubercular patients. While there, he falls in love with a highly sophisticated woman named Clavdia Chauchat. It is love on sight for him, but they are strangers and he is so quintessentially conventional that he cannot bring himself to approach her.

He sublimates his passion by reading books on biology and physiology. With the terrible thoroughness of a man who is German, an engineer and in love, he traces Clavdia Chauchat back to her evolutionary origins. Such behavior is not un-characteristic of lovers. If you read through the history of poetry, you will find that the first thing a man feels when he falls in love is an anxiety to arrive at a working definition of the woman he loves, to know exactly what he has got himself into. This anxiety accounts for all those catalogues of female attributes and qualities that stud the pages of poets such as Shakespeare and John Donne.

Hans Castorp is no trifler. He is a hero of definition, if there ever was one. He begins his appreciation of Chauchat at the moment of creation, the emergence in the world of living matter. Then he works his way up through unicellular ani-mals, through pterodactyls and sharks, to Chauchat. The way he sees it, a molten mass flew off from the sun two billion years ago, cooled, and eventually produced life expressly so that he might meet his beloved Clavdia.

Castorp makes Chauchat's acquaintance on a kind of Walpurgis Night, the one day in the year when the sanitarium's patients are allowed to drink, dance and make merry. After fortifying himself with champagne, he kneels at the feet of Chauchat, who is sitting, and with closed eyes, he propositions her. Now, God knows, there is nothing very new in most propositions, but in the course of his researches, Castorp has stumbled on the ultimate truth about men and women. He loves Chauchat for her essence, for the fact that she *is*, for the two-billion-year-old history of their intimacy. Here is what he said to her (the passage is in French, and I apologize for my translation):

"Consider the marvelous symmetry of the human edifice, the shoulders and the haunches and the breasts flowering from one side to the other on the bosom, and the ribs arranged by pairs, and the navel in the middle of the softness of the belly. . . . Consider the shoulder blades stirring under the silky skin of the back, and the spine which descends toward the cool and twin luxuriance of the buttocks and the great branches of the vessels and the nerves which pass from the torso through the ramifications of the armpit, and how the structure of the arms corresponds to that of the legs. Oh, the sweet regions of the interior joining of the elbow and the back of the knee, with their abundance of organic refinement under their cushions of flesh! What an immense feast to caress them, these delicious places of the human body. A feast after which one would die without regret! Yes, my God, let me smell the odor of the skin of your kneecap, under whose ingenious articular capsule a glistening oil is secreted! Let me touch devoutly with my lips the femoral artery which throbs in the front of your thigh and divides lower down into the two arteries of the tibia!"

Now, that's what I call a compliment. It joins the physical and the metaphysical in what I would unabashedly describe as the sweet mystery of life. Wilhelm Reich said that character is the body, and if you take Freud's "anatomy is destiny" and extend it equilaterally to embrace both sexes, there is poetry in the remark.

Chauchat recognizes a rare compliment when she hears it, and she returns one that is just as remarkable. After allowing Castorp to spend the night with her, she gives him as a souvenir an X-ray photograph. Not a flattering studio portrait or a pinup picture, but an interior view of her self in all its frailty and strength, a view in which her flesh is an aura, a ghostly suggestion. She takes up Castorp's compliment, savors it, qualifies it and complicates it, much as a modern woman might.

The Boy Who Was

a Platonic Essence

"*What* do I tell him?" my friend asked. His seven-year-old son was not represented in the school magazine. "He's been writing for three years, and I've always told him his stories were good."

My friend is an editor, a rather famous editor, at a leading publishing house. "You know they're good," he said. "You've seen them."

"Yes, they are," I agreed. "They're extraordinarily good."

"Can you tell me why the magazine didn't accept one of them?"

"I can give you a few surmises. One is that the person who chooses the stories has a blind spot or an incorrect notion of what a seven-year-old boy's story should be."

"It's supposed to be a fine school," my friend said. "It's hard to believe that a fine school would choose as an editor for its magazine a person who can't recognize a good story."

"What were the other stories like?"

"Nothing special. The usual thing. Some lame, some cute, some OK. Not one that was really outstanding."

There was a silence while we pondered the situation.

"I think," my friend said, "that my son knows he's good. Not because I've told him, but because he *feels* his stories are right. Even at seven, you know when you're good. Everybody always likes his stories."

"Everybody except the editor."

"I could tell him," my friend said, "that the editor is wrong, that he doesn't know a good story when he sees one. But where would that leave my son?"

"It would leave him feeling that the world is either unjust or highly flawed or prejudiced in insidious ways."

"It might destroy his faith," my friend said. "In the school. In the Establishment. In the world."

"He's a little young for 'silence, exile and cunning.'"

"Do you think I should ask the editor why he didn't take one of the stories?"

"Then you would lose faith in the school, the Establishment and the world."

"What if my son decides that they are right and he is wrong?"

"Apart from the fact that you don't want him to stop feeling his stories are worth writing, there is the question of truth. It's important for a seven-year-old boy to know what is actually what."

"Maybe I could make a distinction. I could explain that the world, the Establishment and the school are OK, but only this editor is a mistake. One mistaken editor doesn't have to invalidate everything."

"Then he'll feel discriminated against," I said. "He'll wonder why the mistake had to land on him. You're asking a seven-year-old boy to forgive an adult, a professional adult, for not seeing something that he can see himself. He would have to be a pretty philosophical boy for that."

"Do you think his stories are too precocious? That the editor felt that the other kids wouldn't understand them or that he didn't fit in somehow?"

"No," I said. "I don't think they are precocious." I thought about his son's stories. I could remember quite a few of them. "They're not precocious," I said. "The thing about your son is that he is so much more vividly seven years old than most boys. He's like the Platonic essence of seven years old. I can imagine this editor reading boys' stories for twenty years, adjusting to the norm, and then suddenly being startled by the apparition of an ideal seven-year-old."

"You mean like larger than life?"

"No. He's not larger than life. He's exactly as large as life. In my opinion—and I'm not trying to flatter you—your son is a model of what a seven-year-old boy should be."

"That's what I thought myself," my friend said. "But I'm his father."

"Try to get inside the head of this editor. He began his career with stars in his eyes, with a wild love for little boys or at least the idea of little boys. Gradually, as the results come in, he modifies his expectations, revises them down and abandons his dream, after a painful struggle, for a more realistic attitude. Then your son comes along with his stories, and all the editor's carefully erected defenses, his ironically disenchanted posture, are threatened. If he accepts your son's stories, he'll have to start all over again."

My friend gave me a close look. "You're not putting me on, are you? This means a lot to me."

"Putting you on?" I said. "Of course I'm not putting you on. I've got a son myself. When he was nine, he made only the second team in soccer."

My friend looked down at his hands. He looked off into the

middle distance. Then his eyes came back to me. "So what do I do?"

"You do what I did," I said. "I picked my soccer player up, all the way up, and hugged him."

Neuroses Are

No Fun Anymore

*W*_{hen} *I* was coming up, my friends and I went to psychoanalysts as one goes to graduate school. We learned to explicate our neuroses as if they were poems, delving into literature, anthropology and mythology in order to do justice to our symptoms. None of us thought of a cure, and I never heard of anyone who was cured. Psychoanalysts in those days were Europeans with classical educations and they respected our privacy.

I am disturbed to see that these time-honored customs are being eroded. The new techniques developed by American practitioners are wreaking havoc among my friends. Innocently returning to the couch to freshen up their anguish, they are being cured before they can say Sigmund Freud.

These brash new therapists in turtle-necked sweaters think nothing of tampering with the lives of their patients, whom they call clients. They make them sit up in chairs, stare them in the face, criticize their voices, their gestures, their breathing and their posture. A few go so far as to pry into their clients' daily behavior, and I have even heard of some who make suggestions.

One after another of my old buddies is being hustled right out of his history. Normality is spreading like a plague among them, and pretty soon I won't have a friend left. Or at least not one that I can count on, for I have discovered that you can't rely on normal people. The least little thing upsets them.

With a neurotic, I always knew where I was. There are only half a dozen symptoms and a prepubescent child can recognize and classify them. We used to live in a cozy, finite world and within its snug confines we comforted one another. But what am I supposed to do with a so-called normal person, somebody who simply lives for what he can get out of life?

I'll give you a few case histories so you can seen what I mean. One of my friends had a compulsion to love. He fell in love every week, sometimes every day, and of course he was always exalted, as only a man in the early stages of love can be. There were no late stages in his loves. He was our bard, our botanical garden in perpetual bloom. Then he fell on a fallow period in which he was out of love for three whole days. He became depressed and went to one of the new therapists.

He is no longer the same man. He has aged, and the light has gone out of his eyes. He put on weight. With a Siamese cat for company, he retires early to a dreamless sleep.

Another of my friends was a novelist whose stories of his childhood made strong men blanch and women sigh. His father and mother were monsters of mythic proportions and his early years were a vast sea of pathos. How many evenings have I envied him his accounts of primal scenes, double binds, toilet-training tortures.

Of course, he never wrote any novels, but he was one of the most fulfilled persons I have ever met. We all looked upon him as a gallant survivor, our vicarious hero—until he became a client. Now nobody ever sees him anymore, but I hear that he writes ordinary novels that sell.

With all these cures, conversation is becoming a lost art. The sweet exchange of symptoms, the talk about the weather of the self, used to be good for an evening. A humiliation, an eruption of vanity or pride, a cruelty sustained or inflicted: these and their inflations were food and drink. And then there was always that beautiful moment, the time when my friends would ask my advice. The asking and the giving of advice are the tenderest, the most trusting of all human transactions. The baby at the breast is nothing compared to it.

Even Freud, who was a pessimist, conceded that the neurotic thinks big. The grandeur of his delusions is the last gasp of the epic or heroic mode in the twentieth century. The rationalization of the neurotic is an unending source of surprise and innovation. His irony is the gaiety of desperation. And where would we be, I ask you, without the paranoiac? Is there anyone else who *notices* things?

These careless new cures will probably mean the end of marriage. All the married couples I used to know were depressed, and it made for quiet, peaceful evenings at home, looking at television together. Sometimes the wife would go and snuffle in the bedroom while the husband ran his hands through his thinning hair. A depressed wife is just what a tired husband needs, and all husbands are tired.

Unless it is kindled by anxiety, beauty can only be cold and statuesque. More than anything else, attractiveness in either sex is a thrilling sense of the other's vulnerability, a feeling that we can come to the rescue. When Francis Bacon said that "there is no excellent beauty that hath not some strangeness in the proportions" he was talking about the body English of anxiety. The huddled shoulders of a shaky man, the apprehension expressed in the neck of an uneasy woman, are enough to break the whole world's heart.

If you stop to think about it, you will see that symptoms are the vocabulary of being, the lineaments of personality. Neurosis is the brotherhood of man. Take it away and we have nothing to say to one another. The human contract contracts to mere brutality. The blue note goes out of what Wordsworth called "the deeper music of humanity."

The situation is not hopeless, however. I am in touch with a group of therapists who feel as I do, who are asking themselves "what have we wrought?" With the aid of a government grant, we are founding the Institute for Regression, a clinic where you can recover all that you have lost. Yes, you *can* go back to the womb. For further details, watch for a full-page advertisement in your daily newspaper.

Queen of the Night

N*ew York City* people don't know how hard we try, out here in the country, to dress up our days. While city life is a supermarket of ready-made symbols, events and occasions, country people have to create their own. We are engaged in an eternal Easter egg hunt for something to respond to, something that will enable us to believe that we have not rusticated our sensibilities.

I'll tell you a story that a friend told me. He is an architect named Robert who designed his own house. Country living is often a love affair with a house, and in Robert's case, he and his wife, Sylvia, fit so perfectly into theirs that the effect was almost sexual.

The new structure had been attached to a large old barn, which Robert restored without altering it. In relation to the house, he thought that the barn was rather like a rectangle, indicating speech, issuing from the mouth of a cartoon character. Inside it, Robert imagined the words thesis and antithesis.

As a final flourish, Robert had added a small tower to the

house, and in this tower hung a bell. They would ring the bell on special occasions, he said: The birth of a child, Christmas, any significant time. Both Robert and Sylvia believed passionately in occasions. Their lives were filled with intimate anniversaries.

The story Robert told me concerned one such occasion: The annual flowering of the Queen of the Night. This was the third year they had observed it. Now that the children were away at school, it had become a family birthday.

Sylvia wore an evening gown of a bronze-colored metallic fabric. Her thick, gray-streaked hair was piled on top of her head to show her long, elegant neck. Robert had on a black velvet suit and a ruffled evening shirt with a velvet bow tie.

The only light in the living room came from the fireplace and from a small spotlight trained on the Queen of the Night. Their taped transcription of Bach's "Musical Offering," in the out-of-print Scherchen version, issued from speakers placed around the room. The cembalo chattered an obbligato.

Last year, Sylvia herself had accompanied the flowering of the plant with improvisations on her own cembalo. They had found the instrument in Europe on one of their trips. Gorgeously painted in gold leaf, it had been so expensive that they sold her Bechstein to pay for it.

Now they sat on a small sofa pulled up before the Queen of the Night. In their hands, they held glasses of Dom Perignon; the bottle rested in a silver cooler.

They knew all about the plant. Robert and Sylvia were the sort of people who researched their enthusiasms. *Selenicereus grandiflorus*: the night-blooming or moon-blooming cereus. They knew that its stem contained a digitalinlike substance which increases the contractibility and improves the tone of the heart muscle. They had read that archeologists discovered the remains of a primitive pharmacopeia, some sixty thousand years old, that included seeds of the night-blooming cereus. Barnett Newman had called one of his paintings *Queen of the Night.* These details gave them pleasure. They liked to think of themselves as people who lived for significant details. Robert was fond of quoting Henry James's remark that the artist was the man on whom nothing was lost.

Selenicereus grandiflorus was a member of the cactus family. It had spiky green stems and leathery leaves on which small wens or tubers formed once each year. The tubers grew into buds so heavy that their weight pulled the leaves down. They bloomed, once only, between eight and ten o'clock at night, and closed again before morning light.

Rarity, for Robert and Sylvia, was a virtue. Robert, especially, thought of the plant as preparing itself all year for that one spectacular effort. Both saw it as one of nature's extravagances, groomed for climax. It suggested a metaphor to Robert, one which obstinately clung to the very tip of his mind and refused to articulate itself. Perhaps, he thought, it was many metaphors and he could not choose among them.

The time approached. The long triangular leaves that wrapped the bud began to loosen their hold and thin strips of pink-edged white showed through. The "Musical Offering" had reached the part in which the bassoon playfully bounced through the theme. Robert insisted that he could see the plant's petals move, as you sometimes see the hands of a large clock jerk from one moment to the next.

Sipping his champagne, he felt a small onset of anticlimax and searched himself. Isn't anticlimax always a part of the thing itself? Isn't it inherent in the dialectic of every process, life and death, yin and yang? He reminded himself to stop intellectualizing, to look.

Slowly, the bud opened, emitting a scent so powerful, so concentrated, as to seem artificial. The blossom's drooping head had risen, like a dog barking at the moon. When the petals flared, a golden tongue thrust out.

Robert waited for himself to blossom, but he felt nothing. His heart muscle, its tone, its contractibility, remained unmoved. Perhaps, he said to himself, we have overprepared the event. Or can it be that I am growing old, that time is queen of my night? I feel only hot and cold.

"Aren't you going to ring the bell?"

Robert looked at his wife and searched for an answer. "It's too late," he said at last.

When Sylvia raised her glass to his, he saw the lines in her lovely neck. We should cling to each other, he thought.

They touched glasses. Sylvia drank. Holding his glass aloft for a moment, Robert leaned forward and poured it into the Queen of the Night.

"What are you doing?" Sylvia asked.

"I don't know," Robert said.

Commuted Sentences

*D*uring the newspaper strike, train commuters who were compulsive readers had to fall back on books. Not being in the habit, many of them went to their local libraries and bookstores and picked up the first thing that came to hand. The results were interesting.

Take Mort Lowenstein, for example, who commutes to a New York City advertising agency. Pausing over breakfast one Monday morning, he said, "I have measured out my life in coffee spoons."

His wife, Sheila, gave him a sympathetic look. "Would you like a bigger spoon?"

After breakfast, and an incisive kiss from Sheila, Mort's spirits picked up. Pausing in the doorway before setting off for the 8:28, he extended a hand as if to see whether it was raining. "Welcome, O life!" he said. "I go to encounter for the millionth time the reality of experience and to forge in the smithy of my soul the uncreated conscience of my race."

"Right," Sheila said. "Don't get caught between the hammer and the anvil."

On the train, Mort joined Ed Wilde, a textiles manufacturer. Ed was reading Kierkegaard. "You know," he said, looking up from his book, "I was experiencing a lot of anxiety this morning, but I see here that Kierkegaard defines anxiety as the dizziness of freedom."

Mort was reading *The Denial of Death* by Ernest Becker. "Anxiety is a small price to pay for freedom," he said. "According to Becker, a full apprehension of the human condition would drive us mad." He paused to let that sink in. "It's the suction of the infinite that pulls us out of shape."

"I wonder," Ed said. "Daniel Bell feels that, in this century, the infinite is going through a period of inflation, like most consumer goods."

Mort plunged into *The Denial of Death*. He wanted to finish a chapter before they arrived at Grand Central Terminal. After forty-five minutes he was perspiring, despite the coolness of the car. "Where are we?" he asked Ed, reluctant to raise his eyes from the page.

"I don't know," Ed said. "As Arthur Machen remarked, a gentleman never looks out of the window."

At the office, the creative director, who was not a commuter, came in with his coffee and perched on the edge of Mort's desk. "How's the presentation coming?"

"It's coming," Mort said. "We are cultivating our hysteria with joy and terror."

"Have you got anything I can show?"

"We have done something," Mort said, "to accelerate the exhaustion of the possibilities."

"Copy? Layouts?"

Mort held up a deprecating hand. "We have known the inexorable sadness of pencils."

The creative director drained his coffee cup. "Is there or isn't there anything on paper?"

"To be or not to be," Mort said, "is a primitive form of thinking."

"Yes, I realize that," the creative director said, "but I have to tell the client something."

"Tell him," Mort said, "that I will do such things—I know not yet what they are—but they will be the terrors of the earth."

The creative director looked relieved. "Good," he said. "That's the ticket."

At lunchtime Mort walked along the street with the client. Studying the despondent faces of men who had just returned from their vacations, Mort said, "I see the boys of summer in their ruin."

The client, who was not a commuter, nodded. "Fourteen games behind," he said. "They'll never catch Boston."

The restaurant was noisy with talk and laughter. "There is nothing so melancholy," Mort said, "as the spectacle of people enjoying themselves."

The client sensed that Mort was working too hard. "Don't worry about the presentation," he said. "Rome wasn't built in a day."

That afternoon Mort put his feet up on the desk and watched his stunning secretary water the flowers in his office. "The difficulty," he mused, "is not how to understand beauty, but how to be able to stand it."

When he rose to catch the 5:20, he bent over his secretary and murmured, "At the violet hour, when the eyes and back turn upward from the desk, the human engine waits, like a taxi throbbing, waiting."

His secretary thought her time had come at last, but before she could frame an answer, Mort was gone.

"Have a good day?" Sheila asked, when Mort arrived at home.

Mort dropped his briefcase, misshapen with books, on the floor and pulled off his tie like a man cutting his throat. "Do not enforce the tired wolf, dragging his infected wound homeward . . . " He had forgotten the rest of the stanza.

Sheila had mixed a pitcher of vodka martinis. "Here," she said, pouring a double. "Let's disinfect the wound."

Mort was quiet during supper. The books were getting him down. These days of disinheritance, he said to himself, we feast on human heads. This bitter meat sustains us.

Supper was late, thanks to the pitcher of martinis, and the children were already in bed when they finished. Aware of the pressures Mort was under, Sheila had put on a slinky dress in which she prowled unnecessarily around the room.

Mort watched her brave vibration each way free. After a few moments, he seized her hand. "Come," he said, leading her upstairs, "we will have a profound evening."

A little later, he exclaimed in a husky voice, "The moon is hiding in thy hair. Thy eyes are the betrayal of bells comprehended through incense. Thy soul breaks upon my lips."

Still later, he said, "What can be beyond love? I want to get there."

"Sleep," Sheila said, yawning. "Sleep is beyond love."

Sunsets

O*ne evening,* when I was still living in New York City, I saw a sunset so splendid that I felt it was too much for me to have all to myself. I wanted to share it with someone, in that kind of reflex that reaches out. I was walking alone on Central Park South, and the sun was sinking beyond the trees. The sight of it struck me so deeply that I felt something like anxiety, as if there must be a meaning in this sunset, one that I had to grasp.

I looked around and discovered that, of all the people on the street, I seemed to be the only one who noticed the sunset. I wanted to seize people by the arm—men, women, children —and shout, "Look! Look at that!" Like a wild-eyed street-corner evangelist, I wanted to chant a crazy sermon on the sunset.

I simply could not let it pass, and so I walked up to a policeman. He was a public servant, after all. "Officer," I said, "look at that sunset."

I'm not sure that the sunset fares much better in the country. You rarely hear people mention it, and in our house, my wife and children look at me with amused tolerance when I urge them to come outside to see a particularly brilliant setting. I can think of only one notable exception: On my last birthday, a friend of ours gave me a box of twelve splits of champagne. She lives in a house that stands on a rise overlooking the ocean. "Every evening," she said, "I sit on my terrace and watch the sun go down while I toast it with one of these. I thought you might like to do it, too."

I don't understand why people in the country pay so little attention to the sunset. They still make a fuss over the changing colors of the leaves in autumn and, to me, the sunset is the autumn of the day. From there, we move into the winter of evening and light our fires as little substitute suns. When it grows dark in the country, people are drawn together, because there is nowhere to go but home. The sunset is our early show, our Broadway, our bright lights.

Of course, sunsets in the city are different from those in the country. In *Herzog*, Saul Bellow has a fine sentence that illustrates this difference: "And Herzog, a solid figure of a man, if pale and suffering, lying on his sofa in the lengthening evening of a New York spring, in the background the trembling energy, a sense and flavor of river water, a stripe of beautifying and dramatic filth contributed by New Jersey to the sunset . . . "

In New York City, the sunset has a dirty face—or perhaps it would be better to say that it wears makeup. The city is electric, abstracted away from the idea of the sun. Years ago, *The New Yorker* magazine ran a cartoon showing two abstract painters looking at the sunset from their penthouse window. One was saying to the other, "Pretty awful, isn't it?"

Perhaps a full view of the sunset takes New Yorkers too much by surprise. Usually, they see it in slices, mutilated by buildings. Like nature itself, the sunset is only a rumor to them, a sentimental affair for which there is neither time nor space in their lives. But it seems to me that this is all the more reason for them to celebrate it, to rush up to their rooftops every day to watch the sun go down. I have a fantasy of the entire population of the city crowded together on their buildings, observing this extraordinary phenomenon and being affected by it. They would be like Moslems, facing toward Mecca, listening to the evening call of the muezzin.

When the Italian poet Gabriele D'Annunzio governed the tiny principality of Fiume, he drew up a utopian constitution that required the people to gather in public squares for one hour at midday to listen to classical music, so they might be reminded of the essential majesty of the human condition. My rooftop fantasy is something like that.

Sometimes when I watch a sunset, I'm tempted to ask whether nature doesn't mean something by it. It seems too special a display not to have some significance for us. There are many schools of thought that hold that everything in nature has a meaning for us, inasmuch as we are part of it. Even Claude Lévi-Strauss, that most difficult of anthropologists, wrote a poetic essay, in *Tristes Tropiques*, on sunsets.

In early civilizations, there were sun gods and cults of sun worshiping. But while we have sun worshipers now, they seem to be no more than narcissists or health faddists. The sense of awe, which is at the root of religion, seems to have evaporated.

While I've never experienced an earthquake, I have twice been in a ship on the ocean during a hurricane and it is a most impressive experience. Joseph Conrad said that to understand the magnitude of nature, you must see the ocean in a storm. I think you might say something similar about sunsets.

If I were to let myself grow metaphorical about the sunset, I would say that it sets us an example. To watch the sun go down is to die a little, to pay your respects to time and mortality. Another day, another—what? What did you do that justifies these fireworks, this riot of color, this cosmic applause?

A friend of mine who is a student of such matters says that many of us have forgotten how to look at things. We see the world passively, without projecting ourselves into what we see. We think, or simply register, our perceptions, instead of feeling them. Our response is rather like a camera's, instead of a painter's. And this failure to make vivid contact impoverishes us, alienates us from nature and eventually from ourselves.

I think we should take our cue from the sunset, which I see as getting the evening off to a propitious start. I am even romantic enough to suggest that the sunset gives us a hint as to how to look at one another, perhaps even see our bleeding hearts. Our days, too, ought to go down in flames.

I intend to practice what I preach. I'm going to call up my neighbors, who will be startled, because I have always kept a discreet distance between us. They'll suppose I have called to complain about something—a dog or a horse—or, worse yet, to invite them to a party and break the truce that has lasted all this while. And then I'll say, "Look out of your window. The sun is going down. It's quite a sight."

Au Pair *Despair*

One of the institutions I hold responsible for undermining the American family is the school system. When they so changed the curriculum that it became impossible for parents to help their children with their homework, we lost one of our last opportunities to win their gratitude and respect.

The new math was bad enough, but when my thirteen-year-old son asked me to help him with an essay in which he had been enjoined to avoid all pronouns, I could see that things had indeed passed beyond my comprehension. I'm not sure I can survive in a world without pronouns.

You can imagine my relief, then, when my eleven-year-old daughter asked me about the French imperfect subjunctive. Here was a subject I knew something about, because when the children were younger, we had an *au pair* girl who spoke exclusively in the imperfect subjunctive.

What I know about it, of course, is that it is incomprehensible, so, evading my daughter's question, I fell into a sentimental reverie about Iphigène and the unforgettable summer she spent with us. In those days, it was considered *très chic* to have a French *au pair* girl whether you had children or not, and slaves to fashion, my wife and I applied to an agency. We are both ardent Francophiles and whenever we need proof that we have a happy marriage, we always cite the two summers we spent in France before the children were born.

Perhaps we expected too much from Iphigène. Besides hoping that she would teach my wife, myself and the children the imperfect subjunctive, I thought, too, that we might acquire from her some sense of *savoir vivre,* that indefinable way the French have of flavoring their life as they spice their cooking. It would be the ultimate course in sensitivity therapy. It even crossed my mind that Iphigène, in the immemorial tradition of Colette, might seduce my son and he would begin his life with the inestimable advantage of knowing how to make love in the imperfect subjunctive.

Because of our special interests, we thought it would be best to get a middle-class, or even upper middle-class girl. The higher the class, the rarer the bouquet. Iphigène was *vraiment* upper middle class: Her mother owned an antiques shop in the Rue St. Honoré and her father was president of an advertising agency. You might wonder why such a daughter would want to work as an *au pair* girl in the suburbs, but in Paris at that time it was considered *amusant* to live for a while with an American family. A girl could dine out for a year or get a degree in anthropology on the basis of such an experience.

Before consummating the affair, we exchanged letters. Iphigène assured us, in impeccable English, that she was nineteen years old, that she loved well children and would work her fingers to the bone. We guaranteed her that we were a representative American family who would lodge her with *tous conforts modernes.* And while *au pair* means "at par," or in exchange for room and board, we agreed to pay her round-trip air fare and an "allowance" of $40 a week.

When we met Iphigène at the airport, she turned out to be a large blonde, and it was then that I began to revise my ideas. For one thing, I could not understand a word of her English, nor could she grasp my French. Well, I thought, gliding smoothly into what was to be an unbroken stream of rationalization, that's all to the good. We'll be forced to speak French and soon we will all be fluent. I could not foresee that, instead of improving our French, she would ruin our English.

Iphigène did not look French—or at least what I imagined to be the typical French look. I had pictured a dark, medium-sized girl with a small face, bee-stung lips and enormous green eyes, fluorescent with irony. I had anticipated someone full-bosomed, wasp-waisted, subtly steatopygous, and standing vibrantly on well-muscled legs with tiny ankles.

I have always admired, too, Frenchwomen's posture, the appearance they give of balancing their parts as African women balance baskets on their heads. They have a way, also, of arching their backs, as if they are stretching voluptuously after just emerging from bed.

Iphigène differed in a few of these particulars. She was flat-chested, and broad in face, shoulders, waist, hips and ankles. Her posture reminded me of someone about to receive a painful injection in the arm, and she moved rather spasmodically, like an uncoordinated person learning to play Ping-Pong. Yet she could not have been altogether uncoordinated, for her first question was *"Est-ce qu'il y a du ski nautique?"*

After some initial disappointment, my wife and I plucked up our spirits. While Iphigène had just arrived, we already knew how to say water ski in French.

She smiled understandingly when she saw our Ford station wagon. I think she regarded it as a kind of truck for taking produce to market. She had brought presents for the children. My daughter, who was two, received a silk Hermès scarf, or diaper; my son, who was four, an eighteenth-century dueling pistol. This last item, especially, seemed rather expensive, but we reasoned that perhaps it was worthless in France without its mate.

Brought up on Empire furniture, Iphigène found our authentic early-American country pieces "most interesting." She asked us if it was true that they were produced by whittling with a penknife, which she pantomimed for us in a version taken from an American movie. When we showed her to her room, she asked for the key to the door, and since we did not have one, we were obliged to call in a locksmith.

From the moment of her arrival, she showed an almost paranoid fear of exposure, pulling her draperies, locking the bathroom door, as well as her bedroom, and traveling the ten feet between these two doors swathed in a thick, floor-length, high-collar bathrobe.

At first, my wife prepared French dishes, but it turned out that our guest preferred Ritz crackers, Kraft's American cheese slices and Sara Lee pound cake. When I went to the refrigerator for my midnight snack, these items were always out of stock. Nor was Iphigène's cooking typically French. While my son would eat almost any hamburger, he drew the line at hers.

She had an original way of dressing the children, invariably putting their left shoes on their right feet, and vice versa. My wife and I were puzzled by this, but then we reflected that the French never did seem to know their Right from their Left.

She showed great ingenuity, though, in entertaining her little charges. They would sit spellbound while she did her nails and brushed her long blond hair. She read them stories, of which they understood not a word, but to my daughter it made little difference and I believe my son enjoyed listening to an adult whose English was inferior to his.

Determined to improve our French, my wife and I attempted to engage Iphigène in conversation. When we spoke of a French book, she said "I have not read it." She had not seen any of the films we saw or visited any of the restaurants we liked in Paris. When she proved to be vague even about the Luxembourg Gardens, I began to doubt that she was indeed from Paris.

The crisis in our *entente cordiale* arrived when my wife showed Iphigène the vacuum cleaner and suggested that she employ it in her own room, to which the reply was "I am not used to do dat." When my wife reminded her of her written promise to "work her fingers to the bone," Iphigène looked at her in genuine perplexity and said, "but dat is only your American slang, *n'est-ce pas?*"

To paraphrase Teddy Roosevelt, you never know a people until you camp with them. A Parisian in Paris is not at all the same thing as one in an American suburb. Like some wines, the Parisian personality does not travel well.

We parted amicably. Some friends of ours in New York City were looking for a suitable person to take their son to the sailboat pond in Central Park. He was a little boy of regular habits who liked to sail only on Tuesday and Thursday afternoons, and they were prepared to pay $150 per week. The sad thing, though, is that we have had to drop them. They've mastered the imperfect subjunctive and we can't talk to them anymore.

Woman of

a Certain Age

"*Why did I* move to the country, an overcivilized woman like me?" my friend asks rhetorically. "I suppose that after the life I've led, I need air. You know when a woman faints in the street in New York, the policemen always push back the crowd and say, 'Give her air. Give the lady some air.'

My memories were beginning to crowd me out of my apartment—it was like an autobiographical warehouse. Now I can spread them out on the grass to dry. The country is the only place for nostalgia. For me, it's always autumn in Connecticut."

My friend is a moderately famous writer of a certain age. She is such an accomplished talker that I simply listen, an arrangement we both find agreeable.

"I think of places as movie or stage sets and New York City is not the right set for me. I don't look good in gray. Gray on gray. It's hard for me to make myself heard in the city: An auto horn can spoil a sentence. City rhythms are wrong, too staccato. I like to move slowly, glissades and diminuendos. I am not at my best jumping into taxis.

"I didn't come to Connecticut to hibernate. I've been single for twenty years and I've loved it, but I've got too much to say to live alone. I'm ready for a man, a nice wrinkled hero between fifty and sixty. Men at that age know how to spend money and how to spend themselves—when to plunge and when to play safe. But the only men I meet up here are reporters who want to do a human interest story on me for the local paper. Human interest!

"I used to attract men because I looked sexy. Now I look intelligent and it turns them off. To understand a man is considered a form of aggression. When they gaze into my eyes, they see the truth. I'm like a shaving mirror. What am I supposed to do—play dumb? I've seen everything twice, or three times, and I'm glad I did.

"Most men chase young women, but what is a young woman? A tabula rasa, a blank page. To go around with a young woman is like wanting to write a novel and being afraid to start it. To be with me is like reading one.

"Some women my age amuse themselves with boys, the kind of boys who look like they're sold in drugstores. At one time, an older woman could attract an interesting young man with her style, but only gay types understand style these days. When anyone under thirty starts coming on with me, he's usually looking for a mother, and you know what's happened to mothers."

My friend passes her hand through her frizzy hair and ruffles it to emphasize her remarkable resemblance to Colette. I wonder whether all talented and mischievous women of a certain age come to resemble one another.

"It's an abstract time and that's what a young woman is—an abstraction. All those hard surfaces, pure geometry. The thing about men today—even the educated ones—is that they've been corrupted by painting instead of by literature. They want Botticelli women, inhuman curves, circles, semicircles, arcs, parabolas.

"They've always resented the fact that women grow softer and softer. Don't laugh—it's true. Kenneth Clark says that Rubens was the first man to paint 'the accidents of the flesh.' What a phrase, 'the accidents of the flesh'! The signs of use, of joy and sorrow, the wear and tear of being. I need a man who appreciates ruins, ruins seen by moonlight. Who wants to look at a brand-new housing project?

"A young woman is an advertisement for eternity, a piece of wishful thinking. When a man is with me, he sees, he feels, intimations of mortality. He's risking his life, it's do or die, any night might be his last. That's existentialism.

"We need a new esthetic. We've had enough hard-edge art. It's time for soft edges to come back, bodies ecstatically blurred, an Impressionist dream. But men are afraid of softness. They think it's catching. I read somewhere—where was it? Oh, yes, in Theodore Roszak—I read that people today have a horror of the organic, of anything gooey, mushy or sloppy. I hope he's mistaken, because that's me all over, gooey with sensibility, sticky with history, dripping with identity, rotten with needs. I'm alarmingly present, as any grown woman ought to be. And if men are cowards, if they're worried about having a custard pie flung in their faces, why, I suppose I'm out of luck.

"Part of the difficulty is that nobody talks anymore—I mean real talk. Young people court each other in dumb show, on tennis courts and dance floors. They talk with their muscles—they're more muscular than the Greeks, for God's sake—and their faces are just jack-o'-lanterns to light up the scene. When I was young, men used to talk to women to get them into bed, but I've known men who got me into bed so we could talk. Of all the so-called erogenous zones, the mind is the most maddening. You give me an hour of talk with a man—the right man—and I'll turn his head."

My friend looks at me and smiles. It is a smile that falls between Mona Lisa and Mae West.

"Where's your wife?" she says. "Is she going to stay in the kitchen all night?"

Dreckhaus

We're going to turn our house into a Merzbau. It's the only thing to do. We have already ordered the plaster.

We got the idea from Kurt Schwitters, a German artist who built the first Merzbau forty or fifty years ago in Hanover, Germany. He, too, was an enthusiast of junk. According to Dr. Werner Schmalenback, Schwitters's biographer, "Wherever he went, he collected used streetcar and theater tickets, worn scraps of paper, bits of wire, rusty tin cans. To find them, he went through wastepaper baskets, ash cans, attics, junk piles; he was always stooping down in public places to pick up things people had thrown away."

Building a Merzbau was somewhat easier in Schwitters's day, when junk was free. Instead of picking it up in the ashcans of Connecticut, my wife and I pay hefty prices for our junk at tag sales and flea markets. Like most Americans, we like to do things on a large scale, and we have expanded on Schwitters's original conception.

We picked up a fifteen-foot deacon's bench, for example, not without difficulty. Instead of Schwitters's bits of wire, we found a metal plant stand that holds 103 pots. From his scraps of paper, we have progressed to a complete set of one of Connecticut's oldest newspapers, *The Domesday Trumpet*.

And now it's time for the plaster. Like Schwitters, we find ourselves overwhelmed by the objects of our enthusiasm. Every surface of the house is occupied, swamped by the detritus of American history—and so, following his lead, we are going to turn it all into a monument.

When Schwitters felt that his collection was tending toward a confusion, a miscellany or a debris, his genius rose to the occasion. He plastered it all over and transformed his house into a huge constructivist sculpture that looked rather like the sets in *The Cabinet of Doctor Caligari*.

When his Merzbau had filled one floor, Schwitters evicted his upstairs tenant and broke through the ceiling. His son, too, was forced to move. The project finally extended from the basement, even penetrating the cistern, to the roof. The side of the house developed a sort of hernia, or balcony, and Schwitters added a windowless penthouse or attic, where he could sleep at the pinnacle of his art.

Some of the areas he plastered over he gave titles to, such as "Cult Pump," "Gallows of Desire," and "Cathedral of Erotic Misery." We intend to do the same. As soon as we have plastered over all our unpaid bills and other unanswered correspondence, we are going to call it "Pulp Mulch."

Since it is not comfortable to sit in, our deacon's bench is slated for a plaster job too. It will be the "Cathedral of Orthopedic Misery." In the hernia or window seat on the side of the house, I thought I might enshrine a novel I have been working on for twenty years. With a dozen big bags of plaster, it would make a good "Gallows of Desire."

Oh, we have grand plans. The guest room will be one of our

first efforts. The fact that there are some leftover guests in it will add a further note of human poignancy. Since it is already hip-deep in toys the children won't let us throw away, we will just flood the family room, if we can get the plaster in a big truck like a concrete mixer.

What a glorious resolution for the sweater my wife has been knitting for my daughter since the day she was conceived. And for the bookcase modeled on a Mondrian painting that I started in the library our first year here. We'll go through the house, room by room. We can all sleep in the attic, which is empty, since we never put anything there. We won't even have to add it on.

While planning our project, my wife and I had a daring idea, one that Schwitters himself would have envied. Why not, we thought, our eyes meeting in a wild surmise, why not plaster over ourselves as well? We've lived beyond our time. We, too, are part of the debris of American culture.

After fifteen years, our marriage is an anachronism. Neither crazed with passion, taut with anger nor gelid with boredom, where can we go from here? Sociologically speaking, we are already mummified: why not immortalize our condition with plaster, with a death mask of American wedlock?

The children wouldn't be orphans: we'd plaster them over too. They're just as out of step as we are. My thirteen-year-old son still thinks I'm the smartest, strongest father in Connecticut. He enjoys my company, poor little fellow. He doesn't even seem to mind his mother's attention to me. When I ask him what he's going to be when he grows up, he says he'd like to be a millionaire. It's enough to break your heart.

At eleven, my daughter has reached her sexual perfection and it would be all downhill from here. She loves to cook and wants to be a dancer like her mother. She can't walk without dancing. She still kisses me without reserve, the kind of unselfish, for-its-own-sake kiss that only a child can give. When I go to bid her goodnight, she says, "Lie down with me for a minute, Daddy," and Freud is nowhere in the room.

For a while, goose-pimpled with the grandeur of it all, we flirted with immortality, my wife and I, but I don't think we can carry it off. We are not the stuff of which heroes are made. Neither of us can bring ourselves to plaster over our dogs and the cat, and nobody else could be persuaded to put up with their eccentricities. We'll just have to content ourselves with doing the house.

We're applying for a grant from an ecology foundation to help pay for the plaster. After all, we are the first Americans to recycle junk, not into more junk, but art. We're planning to open the house to the public and charge admission. Since the name Merzbau is copyrighted, we're going to call it Dreck-haus.

Slouching toward Fifth Avenue to Be Born

*F**or those* who live in New York City, fall, not spring, is the season of renewal. Summer is a hot flash, a bath of light and air, a game in which city people try to go back to that other nature, away from their own. Summer is the child in them, but even children get bored with playing. When their heads grow cool again, New Yorkers feel a city-hunger, a nostalgia for their anxiety, for the burden of life.

After a vacation from themselves, they return to find that absence made the heart grow fonder. They love themselves better than before. They have sweated out their dissatisfactions. Now, when flowers die and trees drop their leaves, New Yorkers are reborn.

While I no longer live in the city, I have introjected its rhythms. After a summer in Martha's Vineyard, I am not in the mood for my picturesque house in Connecticut. My engine is tired of idylling, so I take the train to New York. I look contentedly at the backsides of commercial buildings, and as we near the outskirts of the city, I feel like a man about to reopen an affair with a disreputable woman who brings out the best in him.

I plunge down the cleavage of Fifth Avenue, where people rush along the street, hurrying toward themselves. It is like the running of the bulls in Pamplona. Some would say rats in a maze, but how do we know that rats do not enjoy the maze, the delirium of its choices?

There is a feeling of rich improvisation in the air, a sense of the adventure of the street. You might meet anyone here: an old love, your former analyst, an enemy, there's no telling. I was walking on Fifth Avenue with a friend once, a wealthy, conventional man, and his son popped up from a manhole.

I look into the windows to see what has popped up, what fall has in store for us. If the eyes are the windows of the soul, windows are the soul of the eyes. I would like to (I don't know what) in Saks's windows for all the world to see.

Studying the women's clothes, I realize that fashion designers understand the city better than anyone else. The baggy, murky-colored layers they are prescribing for women are like Arab robes to protect them against the heat—the psychological heat—of New York. There is a suggestion, too, of the dance of the seven veils—even the seven types of ambiguity. Doll faces, anklets, wild hair: women are the true graffiti of the city. The new tawdry look is pure denizen. It makes women seem used, secondhand, thumbed over by time and change, disillusioned but not extinguished.

They are not despairing, by any means. Each is looking forward to her annual reincarnation, wondering: Is this my year? Is this it at last? The three-way mirrors of the stores will tell.

The promises in the windows are all for women. For men, there are only pleated pants and narrow ties. And leather, always a profusion of leather, as if men's expectations can be encompassed in wallets or briefcases.

A French proverb says that women deserve what they inspire. Do men? Are we getting what we deserve in pleated pants, narrow ties and leather-wrapped complacencies? Does all the daring belong to women now? The elegant foreign shops offer them another Italian Renaissance, another French Revolution.

It occurs to me that men have traditionally been more unfaithful than women because they are bored with having the same selves all the time. A different woman is one way of reaching for a different self. Their wives, who revise themselves every year, have had the consolation of a healthy narcissism. But as fashion grows more mischievous, as their clothes confirm the present mood of psychological safari, New York women are living up to their look. They are dressed to kill, dangerous to themselves and their men.

These reflections of mine are reflected back by Bonwit Teller's windows, which are filled with clothes that appear to have been designed for whimsical emergencies, for situations not yet conceived.

There are wind-and water-repellent jackets, which are undoubtedly proof, as well, against sexism. They have hoods and high collars that close up to cover the features while women prepare a face to meet the faces they will meet. They have zippers, straps, snaps, buckles, drawstrings, gussets, tourniquets, catheters.

These jackets are worn with mountain-climbing boots—boots that can surmount anything—and with sweaters, skirts and slacks in earth colors and textures, as if for purposes of camouflage in a chic guerrilla war. You could go to Antarctica in these jackets, or to hell.

Each model is interrupted here, there and everywhere by bands of knitted fabrics to allow a maximum of elasticity, as if it might be necessary, at any moment, to leap, to stretch, to flex, to assume unprecedented postures under pressure.

What sort of pressures? Who can say? Who knows what sleek creature, its hour come round at last, slouches toward Fifth Avenue to be born?

Houses

"*I want* you to help us choose a house," my friend said. He was young and recently married. This would be his first house.

I've lived in five houses in fifteen years and as a hobby my wife and I often look at houses we have no intention of buying. I regard myself, therefore, as an expert on the subject.

"The first thing you must understand," I said, "is that choosing a house is not a unilateral decision. The house chooses you as well. It is not simply a place to sleep and eat in, for the house sleeps in you, feeds on you. You are also the recipient of its waste products."

My friend looked at me in surprise. "I had never thought of it that way."

"Every marriage," I said, "is a *ménage à trois* with a house. It goes without saying that a house is a quest, an infatuation, a neurosis, a vice. It is also the first child of the newlywed couple."

"It sounds tricky," my friend said. "What kind of house do you think we could live with, or would live with us?"

"I can't answer that for you. As Freud pointed out, such decisions must come from the unconscious. What I can do is tickle your unconscious a little by describing the three basic kinds of houses and the various postures and transactions they encourage."

"I'd appreciate that," my friend said.

"Good. Let's begin with the early-American colonial, something at least 150 years old. Such a house vibrates, shivers, even staggers with the weight of American history. You can hear the very squirrels in the walls scratching at the past.

"Of course, the spaces in a colonial house are snug, no bigger than a hat box. And they are insulated only with nostalgia, which does not altogether keep out the cold. You can still feel the draft or winds of fate.

"A colonial house is a close embrace. Under your five-and-a-half-foot ceilings you can snuggle in the coziness of a coherent world, a finite universe. God is in the attic and the devil's in the cellar. You know where you stand, even if your knees are bent.

"Your six or seven fireplaces will heat your blood, melt your doubts, reaffirm the combustibility of human passions. You'll bundle in a trundle bed, turn to the Bible instead of TV. You'll be self-reliant, a pioneer, early to bed and early to rise.

"In your true colonial, you are emancipated from the tyranny of the right angle. You adventure in irregularity, in improvisation. Your entire house is made of organic substances, mainly wood, which will mottle, age and decay even as you do, so that you peacefully decline together.

"You can keep vigil in your keeping-room. Your children will be born in the borning-room. Your sons will be named Shem and Jedediah, Eliakim and Zabdiel, your daughters Submit and Waitstill, Rejoice and Patience.

"You'll drink rum, grow your own food and herbal remedies, keep horses, haunt flea markets and auctions. If you're lucky, you'll get hold of an indentured servant who knows how to bank a kitchen stove, draw water from a frozen well, top a tree, butcher a pig and discharge other small household chores."

My friend's face was thoughtful. "It sounds just a bit ascetic, doesn't it?"

"Pleasure," I said, "is usually at the mercy of history. Now, you take your Victorian house and that's an entirely different proposition. Fantasy, ghosts, bombast. Incongruities, séances, table-tapping. Callers and croquet in the afternoon, cards, billiards and masked balls at night.

"Eccentric spaces, architectural extravagances, warts, protuberances, proliferations. Ormolu, lacquer, papier-mâché. Silver-mounted ostrich eggs, elephants' feet, stuffed birds under glass domes. Clocks everywhere ticking the *fin de siècle*.

"A house like a crouching, horned beast. A tension between the hideous and the hilarious, vanity and innocence. If you look hard enough, you may even find a nice example of high domestic grandiose, a style as ornate as a naked nineteenth-century ego.

"A Victorian house inclines toward a pigeon-breasted, throat-clearing, watch-consulting sort of life. It's a ideal setting for choice sentimentality and moral indignation. You'll have to study up on the wearing of rings and the conduct of a cane. To do the house justice, you'll need a dash of genteel decadence: incest, insanity, a few unnatural vices, an equivocal relative or two on the top floor."

My friend looked a little discouraged. He had taken to cracking his knuckles. "What other kinds of houses are there?"

"The modern, of course. You can get yourself a computer-designed, isomorphically congenial house that approximates a topological analog of your personality. A house with thrust, ellipsis, syncopation, an 'aestheto-compassionate phenomenon,' as Paolo Soleri defined it. Such a house is the *dernier cri*, the last cry, of the plan-hungry soul. It is Theodor Reik's 'flight forward,' a straight line from cradle to grave.

"A modern house is a course of therapy, a molting of contingency, an appendectomy, a frontal lobotomy. It cracks space like a nut. It is incontrovertible, a syllogism not yet debased by agony, to paraphrase Paul Valéry.

"A modern house consists of impassioned geometries. Le Corbusier insisted that 'the straight line is instinctive to man and his mind apprehends it as a lofty object.'

"If you like, you can do the whole place in glass. In his book, *Glass Architecture*, Paul Scheerbart remarked that 'a man who daily sets eyes on the splendor of glass *cannot* do wicked deeds.'"

"*Cannot?*" my friend said.

"Well, I suppose it depends on how you define wicked. Every house has its own semantics."

"Is that it, then: colonial, Victorian and modern?"

"To all intents and purposes. Yet there is a fourth kind, the *soi-disant* builder's house, which I hesitate to mention, for it is nothing but a house, a piece of pure, commercial expediency, an all-purpose, comfort-hugging dwelling place with the requisite number of rooms and appliances. A builder's house is a home manqué, an imposture, all things to all men, an architectural incognito, a monument to anonymity, an insult flung in the face of authenticity. It is the sort of structure that shrugs its shoulders and says, 'The style is the man and the house is the box he comes in.'"

"I'll take it!" my friend shouted, and before I could protest, he was gone.

Death of a Store

A *store* failed in our town and my wife and I were shocked and saddened. The signs in the store's windows announcing a bank sale affected us like handwriting on the wall.

It was a good store, one that sold good merchandise and gave good service. The people who owned and ran it were good people. When we saw the bankruptcy signs, we felt that goodness had failed.

It was in this store that we bought our children's clothes from the time they were born. If you go through our family albums you will find, in almost every picture, that our children are dressed in this store's things. Now that it is bankrupt, it seems as if their childhood has been based on a false premise, a shaky assumption.

My wife and I argued aesthetics in the aisles of that store. My son is blond and fair and he could wear anything, but my daughter is dark and I thought that the bright colors my wife preferred tended to overwhelm her more subtle appeal. I leaned toward navy blue and earth colors.

The people in the store never seemed surprised at the

unusual interest I took in these matters. Perhaps they understood that I married late and had looked forward for a long
time to having children.

I think they enjoyed my fussiness. We shared a common
interest in how children looked. We buttoned them into a
philosophy, zipped them into a faith. These people saw children as our pride and joy, as advertisements of our love and
our hopes. They dressed future doctors, lawyers, teachers,
scientists.

They could not adjust to shabbiness or shapelessness, to
the fact that children now want to look tawdry at ten, decadent at twelve. While the clothes they sold were durable
enough to be handed down, kids now will accept hand-me-
downs only from the Army and Navy.

In a sense, optimism was stitched into the clothes of those
racks. When the salespeople handed us our purchases, they
seemed to say Go forth and shine. And, of course, Wear them
in good health.

My wife and I did not go to the bank sale. We would have
felt like vultures. We asked ourselves whether the discount
houses helped close our store. Is everything in life discounted
now? What kind of world are we making in which goodness
cannot survive?

I wonder: Couldn't the owners of the store have made some
sort of appeal to their customers? We rally to save historic
buildings, open spaces, wetlands; might we not have done
something for a store with a historic dedication to the quality
of life?

I would have been willing. I would have been glad to pay in
advance for the clothes I would have bought in the coming
year. If enough regular customers had paid in advance instead
of letting their bills drag on for months, something might

have been done. I have a friend in New York City who is a big man in the clothing industry: I could have got him to come out and offer advice.

But perhaps this is all beside the point. Perhaps, in our time, goodness is bad business. It may be that the people in that store gave us too much for our money. Their courtesy, their time-consuming attention to us, were too expensive.

We haven't told our children about the failure of the store. In a way, I think I'm afraid to hear their answer. I cannot bear the idea that, with the notorious unsentimentality of children, they might simply shrug their shoulders and say, "That's life."

Unanswered Letters

I have ghosts in my attic, hundreds of them. At night I can hear them shrilling, like frogs in the spring. Sometimes they talk to me in my sleep.

These ghosts are real, not imaginary. They are the spirits of the unanswered letters that I keep in a box up there. I am saving them because I mean to answer them, every single one. It's just that I cannot seem to get started. I am waiting for an impulse or an inspiration. I have been waiting for years.

I read somewhere that Juliette Druot wrote fifteen thousand letters to Victor Hugo from the Isle of Jersey. How did she do it? I wish I could talk to her. Is there something about the Isle of Jersey that is especially conducive to letter writing?

Every now and then I bring down my box of letters and pore over them, determined to get going. I feel the weight of their expectation, all those people who have written to me. I can hear, paradoxical as this may seem, the enormous pregnant silence between us.

What must they be thinking? That I am rude, indifferent, surly? Or perhaps they understand. They know that it is precisely because I take their letters to heart that I can't answer them. There is too much to say, I don't know where to begin.

By now the subjects of their letters to me are no longer strictly relevant. Time has blurred them, subsumed them all under one heading. The issue has expanded from the particular to the general. It has become a question of communication itself.

My not answering their letters implies an insufficient regard for the process of communication, a failure of empathy, or sympathy. I must not let them think that. When I write, I will assure them that communication is everything to me, that I see it as the root of the I-Thou relationship, as the trait that above all others distinguishes man and sets him apart.

Philosophers have variously defined man as a rational animal, a political animal, an animal that laughs, and so on. I would call him a communicating animal, an animal that writes letters. I will tell these people who have written to me that I am grateful to them for having reached out. Their letters touched, warmed, comforted, nourished, stimulated me.

Living out here in the country I have almost forgotten how to talk. The sound of the human voice has become as remote as auto horns. Didn't Robinson Crusoe forget how to talk?

I've got to be methodical. It is the only way. I will count the letters, allow half an hour for answering each one, then set aside the necessary time. I look at the box in despair. So many of them.

Why not write one all-inclusive letter to everybody? Isn't

the message the same? I value you. We must stay in touch, we must cling together. We are all we have.

No, that won't do. I always feel frustrated when I receive philosophical letters. They don't give you any idea what the person is doing. They don't contain any news. I wouldn't want my letters to be like that. I will put everything in them, everything.

I imagine myself writing a letter, my hand racing across the page, my thoughts singing. I use a pen with a thick nib, black ink because it is more serious than blue. I sign the letter with a flourish, press the flap of the envelope with an air of decision. The stamps I bought years ago are no longer the right denomination, so I use two instead of one. When I drop the letter in the mailbox, I feel a rich sense of closure.

But isn't there something sad, too, a sense of an ending? Some delicate balance, some beautiful tension, is destroyed. The feeling of possibility is gone. Can any letter answer our expectations? Can heard melodies be as sweet as unheard ones?

Perhaps I should wait just a little longer. Letters, like wine, improve with age. A friend once told me of his experience making a documentary film in Italy, in a monastery. The monks in this monastery had taken a vow of silence and the only time they heard the human voice was at Sunday dinner.

On this occasion twenty minutes was given to the reading aloud of mail received by the monastery. Apparently the correspondence came in at a faster pace than the reading, for according to my friend the letters they listened to while he was there were more than fifty years old.

And the monks' faces, he said, were radiant. Removed by time and distance, the letters took on a magical quality.

Those people who wrote to me, they know that I am preparing my answer. They are looking forward to it as much as I am. When the day's mail arrives and my letter is not among them, they nod their heads and smile, a deep, understanding smile. We realize, my correspondents and I, that these things are complicated.

Al Pacino

Meets L. L. Bean

We take the Jeep, of course with its four-wheel-drive, winch, and side-mounted pick, shovel, axe and crowbar. In their Bean Vagabond Packs, my wife and daughter carry the Stanley Vacuum Bottles, the Frontier Camp Ware and the food. The Folding Camp Table (seats four) is my responsibility, while my son is charged with the Smoke 'N Pit Barbecue.

My wife wears her L. L. Bean Trail Model Pants, a Braided Seine Cord Belt, brown Grasshopper Slipons, a blue Fishing Shirt and Kangol Tropic Cap. My eleven-year-old daughter elects a Bean blue denim "Fan Flair" skirt, Olof Daughters Clogs, and a red gingham checked shirt. My thirteen-year-old son leans toward Lee Riders, a red River Driver's shirt, and Eaton Running Shoes. I am rather spiffy myself in my Kenya Cloth trousers, Warden Jacket, Wilderness Boots and Allagash Hat.

The line of moviegoers stretches from the theater down through the village green to the outskirts of town. It is a colorful scene, a Breughel-like catalogue of L. L. Bean ingenuity, lit by Jet Magic Lanterns, bonfires and flares. Camp

164 /

cots, deck chairs, sleeping bags and pup tents dot the landscape.

Over the barking of dogs that have followed their families to town, we hear the familiar thunder of Land Cruisers, vans and dune buggies, the throaty cough of the last convertibles and the clatter of hooves as the horsey set gallops up. The local dialect rises like bird calls through the cacophony.

Some of the people in line jog in place, while others do gymnastics or yoga. The full-lotus position is in full flood among the meditators. Judging by the position of their feet, those in the pup tents are engaged in friendly wrestling matches.

Because most of us here once lived in the city, we are nostalgic about standing in line. It brings back, with a bittersweet pang, the coziness, the deep, oceanic feeling, of the subway during rush hour. This is why we all come so early. In a town zoned for two acres, we live so far apart that we are starved for the sight of a human face.

Someone near us is playing a washboard and thimble and the fellow with him on the spoons is terrific. Young and old folk dancers execute some very pretty figures. There are jug bands, too, and musical saw combos, in addition to the usual banjos and guitars.

It's a pleasant sight to see infants nursing or peeping out of Bean Boat and Tote Bags, Wood Carriers or rucksacks. Their shrill cries mingle contrapuntally with the rhythmic calls of the popcorn, sugarless candy and fruit-juice vendors.

The wind carries savory smells of steak, spareribs, fried chicken, barbecued lobster and soft-shell crab, and every kind of fish, all spiced with the acrid fragrance of wood smoke, charcoal and lighter fluid. Camp tables and gay picnic cloths make a crazy-quilt pattern on the grass. We are happy to be here.

The film, as usual, is a science-fiction one. We see only science-fiction films up here. This month it is *Bobby Deerfield*, starring Al Pacino and Marthe Keller. Last month it was *Three Women*, featuring Shelly Duvall and Sissy Spacek. Things are a little late getting up here, but we don't mind. We understand that they have to come a long way.

When *Bobby Deerfield* starts, you can hear a pin drop, for we take our movies to heart. For the country dweller, going to the movies is the reverse of going to the zoo. In a sense, we are animals in a natural state, wagging our tails at the mysterious or fabulous doings on the screen. I suspect that, in our innocence, we often respond inappropriately, but how can we tell? In science fiction, anything is possible.

Right now, for example, we have come to a wonderful moment in *Bobby Deerfield*. First, let me explain that Al Pacino is a racing-car driver and Marthe Keller is a racing-car groupie who falls for him, or perhaps the other way around. Anyway, here they are, in bed together and she is sleeping while he leans on his elbow and watches her. Even with her eyes closed, when most people look so vulnerable and childlike, Marthe Keller looks sophisticated and inscrutable. Of course, I am only guessing, but I get the impression that Al Pacino is touched by her inscrutability. At any rate, he reaches over and strokes her hair.

Imagine our consternation when a big hank of her hair comes out in his hand. With a single collective intake of breath, the audience waits to see what he will do. The tension is unbearable as he looks at the hair in his hand without batting an eye. When he takes it and presses it back on her head, the whole theater goes wild. Cheers, whistling, stamping, hats thrown in the air. Applause so explosive that it shatters the bulbs in the red exit lights.

What control that Al Pacino has! When he presses the hair

back on Marthe Keller's head, I defy you to tell what he is thinking. The expression on his face does not alter by so much as a millimeter. Because they have never seen a movie in which people's expressions do change, my children cannot fully appreciate the scene, but I'll try to explain it to them later.

In a way, that is the best part, the discussion back home in the next four weeks, the careful answering of the children's questions, the comparative anthropology of the emotions, the exploration of cultural differences.

"But why, Daddy?" they ask. "Why didn't he say anything when her hair came out? Wasn't he surprised or sorry? Couldn't he catch a contagious disease? Was he too sleepy to care? Did he think he was dreaming? Maybe he didn't really like her? Could it have been a wig?"

"No," I answer, smiling tolerantly. "You must realize that there are more things in heaven and earth, as Hamlet said, than are dreamt of in your philosophy. You can't just pluck out the heart of Al Pacino's mystery the way you spit out a cherry pit."

"But why do they like each other?" my daughter asks. "They don't seem to have much fun. Besides, she's taller than he is."

"You wouldn't catch me going around with a bald-headed girl," my son says. "That guy is a pervert."

"Years ago," I tell them, "before you were born, even before I met your mother, I used to know people in New York who were a little like that. Science fiction, you must realize, is an extension of existing trends."

My daughter giggles. "Oh, Daddy," she says. "You're the biggest fibber in fifty states."

A Middle-Age
Moment of Truth

Carrying a large plastic garbage can, I was cleaning up that part of my property that is on the other side of the stone wall. Legally, this does not belong to me, it's town property, but I regard it as mine because it surrounds my house and I take care of it. I make this trip with the garbage can several times a year.

Beer bottles and cans, soft-drink bottles and cans, paper bags containing the refuse from a meal, empty cigarette packs, plastic coffee containers, newspapers, magazines: these are the usual harvest. This time, as is often the case, a couple of beer bottles had been thrown against the trunks of trees so that sharp fragments of glass were scattered on the ground.

I remembered as I picked them up that, when she was quite small, my daughter was walking barefoot in the grass and cut her foot on such a fragment, which was on our side of the stone wall. I brooded once more on the kind of person who got a kick out of cutting a little girl's foot.

It's a monotonous job, picking up trash, and my mind wandered. I thought of the time, several years ago, when I walked out to my mailbox and came upon two teenagers twisting the stop sign on the corner so that it faced the through street. This was in another house and that was a dangerous corner. There had been several accidents during the time I lived there. Turning the stop sign ninety degrees would certainly increase the likelihood of more accidents.

I was angry, of course, when I saw what was happening, but I'm supposed to be an adult and my anger about some of these things teenagers do is tempered by the recollection of my own adolescence. I approached the boys and said in what I thought was a reasonable tone, "You know, that's a dangerous thing to do."

They looked at me as if I had spoken in a foreign language. I tried again: "There have already been several accidents on this corner," I said. "If you turn the sign around, people who are not accustomed to stopping here may jam on their brakes at the last minute. They could be hit from behind. Or perhaps they'll just go right through from force of habit and collide with someone coming down the other road."

The boys looked at each other and exchanged a smile. What the smile said, as far as I could read it, was: "Listen to this guy. He sounds like an old woman."

They started to move away. I moved, too, so that I blocked their path. They stopped and struck attitudes that they learned from movies. "Don't you understand what I'm saying?" I asked. "Somebody could get hurt here because you changed that sign."

The boy nearest to me started to move away again, and again I blocked his path. I was beginning to lose my temper. "Listen," I said, "I've got two children who wait for the school bus on that corner and I want you to go back there and twist that sign back the way you found it."

The boy put one hand on his hip and dangled the other at

his side. He had big, square, heavy hands. He looked me in the eye. "What are you going to do if I don't?" he said.

In a split second, I changed from a middle-aged man weighing 145 pounds to a force of nature, a father whose children were threatened by a hostile intrusion. I looked at the boy in front of me and at the other one standing a little to one side. They were husky, tough-looking boys, perhaps sixteen years old. Each of them outweighed me by at least ten pounds.

Like most men, I have never thrown a punch at anybody except in self-defense and the last time must have been twenty years ago. The nearest boy was studying me. He didn't look worried. He had what I can only call a brutal face. Neither he nor his companion appeared to be the kind of boy you can reason with.

A judicious observer might have said that I could have walked over to the sign and twisted it back myself, and I wondered about this afterward, but right then, in that moment, I could not do it. I felt that I had been backed up against some private boundary of my own and that I could go no farther.

I realize that it sounds melodramatic, even preposterous, but I felt that I was face to face with evil and that I had to oppose it. I guess I know as much about psychology as the next man, but I was not in the mood for psychologizing. I don't like macho attitudes, but on the other hand I think that sometimes life throws us into situations in which we have to behave like men, whatever that means.

I looked at the nearest boy, who was smirking now, his challenge hovering in the space between us. I felt an electric thrill go through me. It was beautiful in a way, like a dream of flying. I felt indomitable. I'll hit this boy on the bridge of the nose, I said to myself, and when he goes down, I'll turn to the other and see which way he jumps. It never occurred to me that the first boy would not go down, because I was a father and I was in the right.

"You want to know what I'm going to do?" I said. "Well, you just tell me that you're not going to straighten out that sign and then I'll show you what I'm going to do."

The boy's face went slack and his smile passed through two or three changes. The way I was staring at him, I felt as if I was sending death-dealing rays out of my eyes, like one of those creatures in a science-fiction cartoon.

The boy gave a short, derisive laugh which did not come off well, then he walked over to the sign and, with contemptuous ease, wrenched it back the way it had been. They walked off, away from me, and I was left with my anger, my adrenaline, my heart beating like a man in love.

I felt elated. I had won a victory. Not against two stupid boys, but against myself, against the habit of civilization and passivity and rationalization—against the avoidance of action. To be sincere in love, a Chinese proverb says, is to be grotesque. Well, I had been grotesque, and I was proud of it.

Of course, the boys came back that night and tore the stop sign out of the ground and threw it into the bushes. They tore my mailbox out too, post and all, which must have taken some doing, but I just laughed. I'd had my moment of truth, and if this was theirs, they were welcome to it.

It's Not out of Magritte,

It's out of Connecticut

Arriving at night, my friend from the city pauses before entering the house. "Wow," he says, "look at that moon! It's right out of Magritte!"

I look at the moon. It's not out of Magritte. It's out of Connecticut. It's out of this world. It belongs to me, not to the Museum of Modern Art.

While my wife serves a late supper, my friend stands in front of the fireplace and rubs his hands. "Look at that fire!" he says. "It's right out of Dickens!" As he eats, he flourishes his elbows with appreciation. After supper, at eleven o'clock, he declares that he can't wait to get to bed, as if Mother Nature herself waited for him upstairs in a negligée.

In the morning, my friend announces that he slept "fantastically." "Wow," he says, flexing his fingers, "you can *feel* the purity of the air!" After breakfast, we go for a walk. Although the sun is warm, my friend wears a heavy checked shirt under his coat, and World War I aviator boots, which he found in a thrift shop. He tells me that he would like to chop some wood. He searches the ground for a stick. You can't walk in the country without a stick.

He stares at everything with pristine eyes, an anthropologist in the field. He has never been out to my house before. "So this is how you live!" He is astonished that the trees and shrubs grow by themselves, without human agency or chemical encouragement. "Incredible!" he exclaims, throwing back his head before a Norway spruce as a yokel would goggle at the Empire State Building.

He stamps his feet as he walks, making contact with Connecticut. Yet his stride has the crippled, self-conscious rhythm of someone deliberately going nowhere. When we come upon a horse in a field, my friend halts and throws out his arms. "Look at that horse!" He is struck by what someone called "the improbability of animals." His eyes follow the horse as if it was Pegasus or some other mythological beast—a unicorn, perhaps. When cars pass, he regards them as desecrations and delicately averts his nostrils from their noxious exhalations.

At the end of our walk, my friend looks around, turning in a complete circle, seeking to sum up "a tremendous experience." He can't. He hasn't got an explanation for the ineffable.

I invited him out, my New York City friend, because I felt a nostalgia for nervousness. Though I have lived in Connecticut for fifteen years, I haven't yet expunged the New Yorker in me. As much as I love the country, I sometimes feel that I am on the margin, that I can't touch the nerve center from where I stand. I'm afraid of rusticating, of letting vines or roses grow over me. I read too many nineteenth-century pastoral novels. For the sake of what I used to call my sensibility, I need to be needled by New York.

My friend is an extreme instance, almost a caricature of the New York City type, a real denizen. Manic, obsessive, alienated, intellectual, he is a pungent anthology of those qualities generally associated with Manhattan. I invited him out for these very reasons.

It appears, though, that he is not playing the game, that his expectations are antithetical to mine. After packing his lumberjack shirt and aviator boots, there wasn't room in his overnight bag for his critical intelligence, his bibliography. If we are to talk at all, he would prefer to talk in tongues, to exclaim or make onomatopoetic noises like birds or beasts. A serious literary or sociological conversation would be a busman's holiday. He doesn't want to chop logic, but wood.

Ah, well, I can't blame him. We are like cars that pass in the night, going in opposite directions. I watch him appraising my wife, that dauntless settler, that primitive queen of household appliances. I can see that he approves of her, and he thinks she is holding up remarkably well under the circumstances. With my children, my friend is playful and witty, yet I suppose he regards them as part of the landscape gardening of exurban life.

After supper, I suffer the ordeal of the sunset, seen with him, cognac in hand, from the proscenium of my terrace. He describes it to me, of course, as if I could not see it for myself. When the sun has gone down, my friend must go down too, back to the city. He is a bachelor, has never entered into a permanent embrace with a woman or with nature, which to him is also a one-night stand. I drive him to the station, and as the train pulls in, we tell one another what a wonderful time we've had. There is an odd light in his eye, a small flexion of his mouth, as he disappears into the train.

It is only when I am in the car, driving home, that I understand. He was acting, putting on a show for me. He gave it away there on the platform, with that ambiguous light in his eye, that quirky compression of his lips. It must have seemed to him that I had invited him out as I would send for a termite inspector. Do you see anything amiss here, any dry rot? Is this structure solid? Can I sustain it? What could he do but play along?

Back home, I sit in front of the still-glowing fire. My wife is finishing up in the kitchen. The children are in bed. God's in his heaven and all's right with Connecticut. I picture my friend in his apartment in the city. It is untidy and the windows are dirty. There is nothing to see outside anyway. There is only the abstract and unnatural adventure of the city.

I pity my friend because that is his life, and I pity myself because I had to give it up. I bank the fire—what a metaphor!—and go upstairs to kiss the children in their sleep.

Fireplace

O*ur first* conversational impulses exhausted, our minds and bodies lulled by food and drink, we gaze, my guests and I, into the fire.

Each of us sees different things. I watch my friends' faces grow thoughtful as the fire absorbs their vacant eyes. Some of them look melancholy, as if they are reflecting on the fact that all life is only a burning up of energy, that, in a sense, we all go down in flames. For others, the fire is like a Rorschach test: they see in it whatever is uppermost in their minds.

After dinner, there is a spiritual belching. We leave the séance of the table with its associations of family and festivities and retire back into ourselves to wait for our second wind. Temporarily dispersed, we need the fire for a focus. It may be the only thing we have in common at this moment.

Thousands of years ago fire helped to civilize men, brought them together around a common center, softened them with its influence. It is not so very different now. Two hundred years ago this same fireplace cooked the meals of the people who lived here. While I use this for a living room, a place to cook up conviviality, it was a kitchen to them, the guts of their way of life.

For us now, fire is not a necessity, but a ritual, one that has lost much of its grandeur and terror. We no longer sacrifice virgins to fire to propitiate cruel gods, nor do we burn witches. Yet there is something numinous about fire which hypnotizes us. If we have lost the habit of worship, perhaps we still hover on the edge.

In my own mood of post-prandial melancholy, I ask myself whether even this mild obeisance to the fire may not be obsolete, for few of us here have kept that old feeling for hearth and home. We are more like what Spengler called "intellectual nomads." Of the dozen guests in the rooom, I count six who have already abandoned one conjugal hearth for another.

Yet not one of them would buy a house without at least one fireplace. What is the country without a fireplace? they ask, as if we were Neolithic men and women. It is more important even than a swimming pool. Things have come to such a pass that we are always either heating up or cooling down our errant spirits.

When I was a bachelor, my Greenwich Village apartment boasted a brick fireplace and I used to buy bundles of logs from an ancient Italian and carry them up four flights of stairs. Even then, a modest evening's fire cost $20, or four $5 bundles. This was not counting kindling, which sometimes came in the surrealistic shape of women's high heels. Rejects from shoe factories, these hardwood heels burned very well, though their symbolism left something to be desired. A fire in New York City was almost as dear as love itself. One night I expended $60 worth of wood in honor of a young woman who was neither a virgin nor a witch.

A fire burns well only on the ashes of many former fires, and here is a profound metaphor for those prepared to pursue it. If I recall correctly, Freud saw flames as phallic, but I think that the feminine principle has at least an equal claim. A man building a fire is almost as pleased with himself as when he is kindling a woman, and a woman being warmed hisses and crackles like a fire. Good fire-builders are looked upon as macho, and those whose fires die out must suffer the opposite inference.

I find firelight more flattering than candles. Only Camilles or the dead look dramatic by candlelight, while in the glow of my fire, everyone is flushed with promise, flickering with change, with a shadow-play of mixed feelings. There is a heady hint of cannibalism in the room, as if we might like to consume one another. Why else is that woman warming her haunches on the hearth?

Conversation sputters and bursts into flame. We have thawed our cool thoughts—so much more heat-resistant than our bodies—to room temperature. I feel a blaze of affection for my friends and for my home. The fire has dried out the dampness in our souls, the winter in our hearts.

Shaggy-Dog Story

This is a shaggy-dog story. It raises certain shaggy questions about love, responsibility, guilt and the sanctity of canine and/or human life. The dog in question belonged to a couple I know. She is a concert pianist, and he is a psychotherapist. They had not planned to have a dog. In fact, their respective careers kept them so busy that they postponed having children.

However, a friend who was going to Egypt on a year's sabbatical offered them free a beautiful German shepherd female from a famous line of champions. Laura was tempted. They lived in a suburb, and she felt that the dog, whose name was Vandal, would be company for her while Edward was at his office or giving training workshops on weekends. After some hesitation, Edward agreed. Both were influenced by Vandal's extraordinary beauty. Like many young couples, they thought of a dog as a first step on the way to parenthood.

Vandal turned out to be so pleasant to have around that Laura and Edward decided to breed her. They chose a male puppy from the litter of six and named him Goldberg because Laura was getting up Bach's *Goldberg Variations*.

A few days after the puppy was weaned, Laura and Edward went out and left him in the basement with his mother for a few hours. When they returned, Goldberg was lying on the floor, which was covered with blood. They rushed him to an emergency clinic at a veterinary hospital, where they were told that Goldberg has been born with a condition called intussusception—his intestine was telescoped in a way that prevented him from digesting food.

They called the breeder who owned Goldberg's father, and she advised them to have the puppy put down. The veterinarian described an operation called a laparotomy. After such surgery, he said, Goldberg would have a good chance to lead a normal life.

Laura and Edward agreed to the laparotomy. They were quite concerned about Goldberg and often talked and thought about him during the week that he was in the hospital. They were advised not to visit for fear of exciting him.

They took Goldberg home with great tenderness, but it was soon apparent that he was suffering from acute diarrhea. They cleaned up after him without resentment, walked him almost hourly and tried in various ways to comfort him. The vet gave Goldberg a different diet, and his condition grew not better but worse.

Cleaning up after Goldberg became a considerable chore. Laura and Edward dreaded their mornings. It was summertime, and they experimented with leaving Goldberg in their fenced-in yard at night. His barking woke them and they feared for their neighbors.

They began to feel the effects of disturbed sleep. Edward was working on a book, and it was not going well. Laura was not making much progress with the *Goldberg Variations*. They kept jumping up from their work to see how the puppy was feeling.

There were more visits to the vet. Goldberg was taken to the hospital and given extensive tests. Other vets were consulted. Various diets and drugs were tried without appreciable effect.

Goldberg's illness dated back to early May. In August, Laura had two severe nightmares about the dog's condition. She and Edward talked about the humanity of having Goldberg put to sleep, but in spite of his unremitting illness he was still playful, alert and intelligent—"so brave," as Laura put it—and they could not bring themselves to put him down.

Goldberg had an endearing way of sitting under Laura's grand piano with his head cocked, as if he was listening to her play. She told Edward that she could clearly see sadness in Goldberg's eyes, and Edward said that she mistook a physiological alteration for an physiognomic one. Laura insisted that when Goldberg wagged his tail she could tell from his expression that the effort caused him pain. Even Edward, who tried to maintain an appearance of objectivity, had to concede that Goldberg's infrequent high-pitched bark, which did not seem to be caused by anything external, had an interrogative note.

In their visits to the vet, Laura and Edward became acquainted with a circle of people whose dogs also had chronic problems. They found themselves eating dinner with these people and talking all evening about their dogs. One woman whose golden retriever had hip displacement revealed that she had taken it to be Rolfed, a controversial system of deep massage for emotionally disturbed persons, based on an assumed correlation between physical and mental states.

When Laura and Edward were not talking to other people whose dogs were afflicted, they examined their feelings about Goldberg and discussed him in all sorts of contexts. Edward tried to extrapolate what he knew about human suffering in order to imagine what Goldberg was experiencing. Cautioning himself against anthropomorphism, he recalled nevertheless a remark by Kurt Koffka to the effect that even a psychologist likes to forget on Sundays that his dog is little more than a chain of conditioned reflexes.

Then one day Edward wondered whether the friend who gave them Vandal had actually gone to Egypt or had simply wished to get rid of her. One evening, with tears in her eyes, Laura exclaimed, "It's our lives against Goldberg's! "

With his distended belly and emaciated body, Goldberg was no longer a handsome puppy. Laura and Edward unconsciously modulated their affection for him in subtle ways. He evoked a different kind of love now, and Edward was uncomfortably reminded of his compassion for certain of his patients. Laura said that she would never be able to play the *Goldberg Variations.*

In the midst of one of their discussions, Edward announced to Laura that he was not one of those stereotypically guilty liberals who felt that he had to take the world's sorrows on his shoulders. He said that he had work to do, that their unwillingness to put Goldberg down was the worst sort of sentimentality, and cruel as well. Laura accused Edward of trying to force her to make the decision.

"Think of all we've done for Goldberg," Edward said. "Try to see the situation against the larger scheme of things."

"I know, I know," Laura said, "but the larger scheme of things is out there, and Goldberg is here."

In its conclusion, Goldberg's story very nearly satisfied the conditions of classical tragedy. One of the people Laura and Edward had met in the incurable-dog set told them of a noted pathobiologist, a man who was said to be the world's leading

authority on the gastrointestinal problems of German shep-
herds. This pathobiologist had just received a grant to help
finance further research in the field.

Edward phoned him. The pathobiologist offered to accept
Goldberg on these terms: The dog would be kept on a farm for
several months while every possibility for study and cure was
explored. If he could be cured, Goldberg would be sent back to
Laura and Edward. If he could not, he would have helped
veterinary science.

It is several months now since Goldberg was taken to the
pathobiologist. Laura and Edward have not heard from him,
and from time to time they write reminders on their
blackboard in the kitchen to call.

How to See, Walk, Sit, Play and Ponder in Your Garden

Last summer, I learned the proper way to see, walk, sit, play and ponder in my garden. I realized that an unexamined garden is not worth growing. For fifteen years, I've been simply taking my garden for granted, shambling around with a blade of grass in my mouth, indiscriminately smelling the flowers and generally behaving like a bumpkin.

My eyes were opened by two books: *Eccentric Spaces,* by Robert Harbison, and *The Genius of the Place,* by John Dixon Hunt and Peter Willis. According to these last two gentlemen, a garden is a calendar of taste, explicitly designed to express its owner's philosophy, politics and aesthetics. In Alexander Pope's words, it should conduce to "the Feast of Reason, and the Flow of Soul." James Thomson apostrophizes the garden as a place where "all the Tumult of a guilty World Tost by ungenerous Passions, sinks away."

When I read in *Eccentric Spaces* that "the activity peculiar to the Boboli Gardens is erroneous wandering," I experienced a shock of recognition. All these years, I had felt that it was a mistake for me to go strolling in the garden instead of staying indoors and finishing my novel, but now I see that this is precisely what gardens are for. Erroneous wandering—what could be a better preparation for the modern writer?

The Tivoli Garden, Harbison said, "makes geometry quietly hilarious." Was there any reason why my garden should not do as much? I was on the point of planting three small dogwood trees that I bought at a sale. The fellow at the nursery advised me that three trees were best disposed in a triangle and I asked myself what sort of triangle would be quietly hilarious.

The *Encyclopaedia Britannica* lists several kinds of triangles: right, equilateral, isosceles, scalene, acute and obtuse. Both the right and equilateral triangles I dismissed as too stringent. Anything obtuse was eliminated by definition, and acute seemed to have a tense or aggressive connotation. Isosceles suffered from a monotony of symmetry, much like equilateral. A scalene triangle, however, has three sides of unequal length, and if that isn't quietly hilarious, I don't know what is.

"In a French garden," Harbison observed, "trees actually feel laconic, as if on this floor conversation might be expected." Here, I regret to say, my garden is unavailing. Conversation has never really flowered; it has, in fact, consistently fallen below my expectations. Why, I don't believe I've ever heard so much as an apothegm out of doors. Not even a *mot juste*. Yawning, in fact, seems to be the forte of my garden—but I begin to understand. The trees are too boisterous, always soughing in the breeze. They're positively garrulous—no one can get a word in edgewise. I propose to take measures, however. I'm drawing up a plan with my arborist, who agrees with me.

Willis and Hunt have me concerned about the politics of

my garden. The great English gardens, they declare, embodied the idea of English liberty in their democratic inclination toward the natural, while the regimented blooms of Versailles were victims of French absolutism, under constant threat of decapitation. Since I am not terribly political, I find this a vexing question. Should I strive for a New Left effect of integrated disintegration? Shall I truck in some nonindigenous plants? Or would it be permissible, far from the madding crowd, to indulge the private nostalgia of a decadent pastoralism?

I'm fortunate in already having a folly in my garden. For those who are not conversant with the arcana of gardening, a folly is an architectural extravagance dear to the fancy. My swimming pool, augmented by its ha-ha, is an ideal modern translation. If I drain it in the winter, the pool can double as a grotto, which was all the rage in Pope's time. The *pièce de résistance* was to have a hermit inhabiting the grotto—to dramatize it, so to speak. Usually, these gentlemen were hired for the purpose, and I am thinking of advertising for a retired executive.

A ruin, too, is indispensable to the compleat garden, and I believe my barn will qualify. In the opinion of an early authority quoted by Willis and Hunt, a ruin "excites an inquiry into the former state of the edifice" and brings to mind "the fleeting Forms of Things and the Decay even of this our Globe."

Perhaps the fondest conceit of every ambitious garden was a Temple of Love, adapted to dallying with the fair sex. Generally, these were miniature marble confections in the antique style, but I believe I have hit upon a happy innovation, a modern touch responsive to the spirit of our age. Inasmuch as one of my automobiles has become more or less stationary, I am going to have it towed out into the garden and enshrined in a secluded corner.

I have offered to address the local garden club with a view toward raising the tone of neighborhood culture. Like all schemes for public improvement, this can only be a gradual process. There will always be a few atavistic types who continue in the savage state, content to chew the cud of their conplacency and let their grounds go wild.

They think nothing of exposing their families and neighbors to "rude nature," as an eighteenth-century writer phrased it, "with its warts and boils," its "pudenda," its "uncovered parts."

Many gardens, I understand, were planned to be "read" like poems. Some of them even succeeded in spelling out horticultural puns and epigrams. While I haven't yet worked up an epigram, I pride myself on this pun: "It takes a lot of green stuff to grow a proper garden."

Gifts

W*hen I* innocently remarked, months ago, to my wife that I had never owned a decent shaving brush, the thought was carefully filed away, and under the Christmas tree appeared an enormous brush of "genuine live badger hairs," encased in a horn-rimmed handle.

Lathering my face with this majestic tool, I realize how lucky I am in never having had to face, as a husband, the horror of an inappropriate gift. To be married to misunderstanding would be a fate worse than—well, not death, but bad enough.

There are few things more subtly distressing than an inappropriate gift from someone close to you. In the moment of opening it, you feel betrayed. You examine the person who gave it to you, look the gift horse not in the mouth, but in the soul. Behind your assumed smile, you wince and wonder: how could you make such a mistake about me? I counted on you, of all people, to understand me.

For that is one of the best things about love: the feeling of being wrapped, like a gift, in understanding. Someone else knows exactly how you feel. Your individuality has a witness and an advocate, a person who will testify to you. You are not alone. Love connects your loose ends, completes your circuits, keeps you from draining away into nothingness.

To be given something that does not pertain to you implies that you are loved for the wrong reasons. You are chosen by accident, for qualities that lie not in yourself but in the other person's imagination.

In an indistinct way, I realized that Christmas gifts were metaphors as early as my seventh year. I had dreamed of a sailboat, a sleek, dark-brown shape with tall white sails, but under the Christmas tree was a low, solid canoe, occupied by two chunky Indians.

My mother did the Christmas shopping in our family, and I recognized her hand. To her, a sailboat was a flighty, racy, insubstantial object, its canvas billowing with suggestions of flight and exotic places. She had not brought a son into the world to send him to the Antipodes. She meant for me to paddle my way through the shoals of life, keeping close to the shore, advancing myself through the force of my own exertions.

While my wife, who is a mother too, rarely uses a metaphor in speaking, she is in her glory at Christmas. When we were first married, she gave me an elegant suitcase so enormous that, when it was filled, few porters could lift it. "We're going to travel a lot," she said, packing all her expectations into that capacious bag, which, after all, did prove to be a bit larger than life.

In the early years, her gifts held out all the romance that my mother had so carefully repressed. She gave me a beautiful painted chest to hold in reverence a proliferating pile of manuscripts. Then there was an eighteenth-century harvest table, pun intended, on which they were to be sown and reaped. These were followed by a leather-bound notebook from Florence and elegant pens, responsive to the touch, in a range of wide and narrow points.

After a dozen years of marriage, Christmas took on a slightly altered inflection. The world-traveling artist turned into a *paterfamilias*. I was given a floor-length, velvet-textured bathrobe, both warm and sensuous to the skin, the kind of robe English lords, or even kings, may be seen wearing on television.

Domestic life was being glamorized. I received a dashing coat, all zippers and lapels, in which to walk the dogs. It is one of the many peculiarities of our dogs that they must be walked at midnight, in all weather.

Then, this year, there was the shaving brush. I was wrapped in a thick, velvety bathrobe of recognition and lathered with empathy.

Christmas is an annual challenge to love. Can you see into my secret heart? Do you know the child in me? Have you guessed at my fantasies? Will you give me something I would not have given myself because I was afraid I did not deserve it? Will you *indulge* me?

The most terrible of the inappropriate gifts are not the careless ones, but those that are clearly painstaking. The more effort that goes into the mistake, the wider it spreads. Spilled love is the saddest of all spectacles.

There are other, lesser errors in giving, like the present that strains for originality and achieves only irrelevance or bizarreness. The disproportionate profusion of gifts that protests too much. The comic gift that confesses a lack of poetry, that evokes Nietzsche's observation that jokes are often the epitaphs of emotions. The practical gift: I knew a woman who refused an eligible suitor because he gave her things like vacuum cleaners. Then there is the unsuccessful homemade or handmade gift that mistakes effort for effect. Or the gift that is uncharacteristic of the recipient in such a way as to imply criticism or a need for change. I suppose there are even ambivalent or hostile gifts which say that if you were the person you ought to be, this would suit you.

Few of us are loved as accurately as we might wish, and perhaps only God could satisfy us in this way. Yet the Christmas season is not only the season of love, but of faith. So let's have a show of faith. Let's wrap ourselves up in our bathrobes and paddle our canoes into the New Year.

Absurdly Happy

---

*W*hile *I* know a few people who are content and a greater number who are holding their own against depression, I can think of only one person in my acquaintance who is actively and consistently happy. You might even say that he is absurdly happy, a phrase invented especially for our time.

He is a painter named Bob Natkin. And the other day I went over to his house to study him and see if I could learn his secret. "How do you explain the fact," I asked him, "that an intelligent, perceptive man like you is so happy?"

"Well," Bob said, leaning back in a splendid Windsor chair until it creaked in protest, "my first impulse is to say that I'm happy because people are buying my paintings. For forty years they didn't buy them and I was a victim of unrequited love. I think that unrequited love accounts for much of the unhappiness in the world."

"Then you think it is your success as a painter that has made you happy?"

"No. I said that was my first impulse. But think of all the successful painters who are unhappy, who commit suicide. There's more to happiness than success. I think it is also a kind of talent for being, an excitement in things."

"Give me an example."

Bob thought a moment. He picked up his glass of wine from an eighteenth-century tavern table and took a sip. "Well, I'm happy because now I have plenty of space for happiness. When Judy and I bought this house, it was tiny. Then we added on a studio that's forty by thirty. Now I stand in there and I can feel myself expand. You know how people say, 'I felt like I was ten feet tall'? Well, I feel like I'm forty by thirty. And we're not going to stop there. Judy wants to build a bedroom over the studio, the same size. She says that an artist's bedroom should be as large as his studio.

"I'm crazy about space because I had to sleep with my uncle until I was four years old. That's another thing about happiness: I think you have to have been unhappy before you can be really happy. You know, I didn't realize what a terrible childhood I was having until my high-school art teacher told me that my mother asked him to flunk me because she did not want me to become an artist."

"Do you think that money has anything to do with happiness?"

"Yes and no," Bob said. "While money can't buy happiness if you're unhappy, it can buy more happiness if you're already happy. As Meyer Schapiro observed, almost every decision in middle-class life is an aesthetic one: how to behave, what to wear, how to decorate your house, where to go, what shape to give to your time, what to eat and drink. Judy and I love to eat, so we bought her an aesthetic stove. It's an architectural object, a Garland stove. But it needed a hood, so I asked a friend of mine, a metal sculptor, to make a hood. Come on, I'll show it to you."

We went into the kitchen, and yes, it was the most aesthetic stove hood I have ever seen.

"You know what I'm going to do?" Bob said. "I'm going to get Judy a pair of padded drumsticks so she can drum on the hood when she feels she has made something unusually good."

"Obviously, you're spending more money that you used to. How do you feel about it?"

"Well, I feel grateful to people for giving it to me in exchange for my paintings, and I feel obliged to spend it as freely as they did. I don't feel guilty about spending money. I look upon it as an experimental or educational thing to do. You know, you have to be aggressive about happiness. You have to invest in it, to go for broke."

"Do you ever feel that you will go broke, that people will stop buying your paintings?"

"No," Bob said, looking around at his work on the walls. "I'm in the museums now, and they would have to admit that they made a mistake. Once you're in there, the chances are you'll stay. The bureaucracy is too unwieldy to get you out. Contrary to public opinion, an established reputation is one of the hardest things in the world to lose. Before a painter is accepted, he has to fight against people's prejudices. After he is accepted, those prejudices protect him."

He sipped at his wine and brooded on his happiness for a couple of minutes. "Actually, I feel very secure. My paintings are scattered all over the world. I exist in Japan! In Zurich! In São Paulo! Think of all the trouble it would be to gather up my paintings and condemn them!

"Besides, Judy is a great painter and it's just a matter of time before people start buying her work. I can feel their prejudices softening already. When they come here, I catch them looking over my shoulder at her paintings. I think women painters are not sufficiently appreciated. It's easier for a man because people are so surprised to find a man making something that moves them.

"With a woman, they are more likely to take it for granted, to think of her art as part of her sexual attractiveness, of her ability to make things that taste good, or do things that feel good. Women are so immersed in art that it's sometimes hard to tell where they leave off and art begins."

"You told me that you worked ten or twelve hours a day. Where do you get the stamina?"

"Art gives you stamina, but I'm trying to develop even more. I go out and run every day. Sometimes, when I overdo it, I get spots before my eyes. I want to paint those spots."

"Are you lonely, a city boy like you, living way out here in the country, working in a large empty studio all day?"

"It's not empty. It's full of the voices of my paintings, of all the victories and defeats I've known there. And then I have my anxiety for company. It's like a radio playing music while I work. I dance to my anxiety. To be happy is not to be without anxiety. I would say that anxiety is the crisis, the danger, of happiness."

"Do you see your happiness reflected in your children?"

At the mention of his children, Bob's face broke into a beatific smile. "I hesitate to speak for my daughter. While I believe she's happy, she's very mysterious to me because she has just turned into a young woman and she dazzles me to the point where I can't see straight.

"With my son, I feel a little more qualified to speak. For

example, I sent him to Europe last summer so he could look at cultures, people, castles, churches, museums—and what happened? He came home and found a girl who includes, who sums up, who epitomizes all those things. She's a museum of what a girl ought to be."

"Tell me about your antiques, Bob."

He smiled. "As you can see, it's a good, but rather curious collection. Judy and I love early-American painted furniture but we have very little room for it because our paintings fill up all the walls. Since Judy's paintings are smaller, we were able to hang them in the original part of the house where the ceilings are low. Then we added on a large living room, which doubles as a gallery, so we could hang mine too. But as you can see, there is still very little wall space, and that's why we buy mostly low things, like blanket chests."

We were in the new living room, which was almost as big as the studio. Between the windows, the walls were covered with Bob's paintings and underneath them was a row of painted boxes and blanket chests that any collector would envy.

"I like to think," Bob said, "that hidden inside those boxes and chests are the histories of my paintings."

He lifted the lid of one of the chests as if to test this notion. Then he laughed. "I suppose people might call me self-centered, but maybe happy people tend to be self-centered, busy with their happiness. Until he is accepted, an artist has to be self-centered. It's your belief in yourself that makes your paintings convincing. To throw off, or pretend to throw off, your self-centeredness after it has worked for you is like repudiating your history, like disowning a part of your personality."

A silence fell across us. I could see by his face that Bob was pondering something. "Listen," he said, "you don't think I'm too happy, do you?"

"Too happy? No. What makes you ask that?"

"I don't know. Sometimes I think there's only so much happiness in the world and I don't want to be a hog."

Snow

While it's all right for cities, I don't feel that we need snow out here in the country. We've already got trees and grass, and snow goes too far, paints the lily. It turns everything into a Christmas card, or a smarmy passage from Dickens. Enough is enough, and too much is parody.

As it is, I can't get my city friends to take country life seriously—and who can blame them? How can I practice "silence, exile and cunning" in a winter wonderland? Such homogenized serenity is death to the writer's sensibility.

After all, it's my land, my property, on which the snow falls, and I don't want it mantled in ermine. I have nothing to hide. I'm opposed to euphemism on principle, and the picturesque has no place in my plans. I protest.

As I said, snow is all right for cities. I didn't mind it there. In fact, I believe that something of the kind is called for.

I was six years old when I first saw snow. Emerging from Pennsylvania Station, I found everything enveloped in feathers, as if all of New York's inhabitants had been absorbed in a pillow fight. In New Orleans, where I had come from, I had seen snow in books, but only lying flat on the ground, not falling through the air.

My father, who had made a strategic reconnaisance before bringing us up to New York, warned us that it was a most foreign place. The people there, he said, poured molasses into their beans. When he reported that it snowed in the North, I received this information with a dignified skepticism, being inclined to regard snow as a substance more metaphorical than real.

Snow gave the city an incandescent light, stronger than the sun in New Orleans, turning it into an all-white world like a new coloring book. As I stood on the steps of Pennsylvania Station looking at the snow, holding up my hands and sticking out my tongue, I felt that I had truly arrived in the North and was immeasurably far from home.

I soon discovered that snow had more uses even than mud. It was nature's own play dough, a plentiful free substance that could be compacted into a ball and thrown at other boys, at girls and at passing vehicles.

In those days, the Sanitation Department was more sanguine about snow. It made no pretext of removing it, but piled it instead into large mounds from whose eminence I and the other boys in my neighborhood attempted to thrust one another. I was pleased to learn that snow was slippery, and when my parents provided me with a sled, I passed my days in belly-whopping.

I maintained a tolerant attitude toward snow even as an adult. I liked the way it brought out a playful, even hopeful attitude in the normally gloomy Northern temperament. It seemed to me that everyone in New York City was continually waiting for something, and that when snow came they seized the occasion and cried, "This is it!"

I remember a heavy snowfall in the early 1960s that inexplicably prompted the city government to declare a moratorium on cars one weekend. I lived in Greenwich Village at the time, and I went strolling in the middle of Fifth Avenue with an absurdly free, dreamlike feeling. Everyone was walking in the street—the sidewalks were deserted—and we all laughed, talked to strangers and behaved like characters in a painting by Breughel.

Snow gave the city's shabby chaos an air of abstraction, like a severe and intellectual modern painting: Malévitch's *White on White,* or something by Ad Reinhardt. Like a woman modestly covering herself, snow drew a sheet over New York's jaded nakedness. It was an expurgation, an erasing of epithets.

Inevitably, the beautiful virgin city sullied herself, fell from grace, scattered garbage like irony through the streets. The blond princess reverted to a swarthy witch, the tabula rasa was disfigured with truth. We had enjoyed the snow in its purity and then, New Yorkers that we were, we reveled in the ugly moral, the knowledge that nothing lasts.

From where I sit now, that last line is not strictly true. The snow out there in the fields looks as if it will last forever. It hasn't even begun to get dirty.

But I have an idea. Instead of doing just the driveway, I'm going to have my man plow the whole six acres, hill and dale, grass and gravel. People may think me strange, but I don't care. If a writer hasn't got the courage of his convictions, he doesn't deserve the name.

Working at Home

"*You* work at home? Oh, you're so lucky!" This is what everyone says, but how would they know when they haven't tried it? How could they guess that I suffer more from distractions out here in the country than St. Anthony did in the desert?

To begin with, there's the noise. Like the philosopher mentioned by Rabelais, who thought he had withdrawn from "the rusling clutterments of the tumultuous and confused World," I too find myself "surrounded and environ'd about with the barking of Currs, prating of Parrets, squeaking of Wesils, chanting of Swans, pioling of Pelicans, gushing of Hogs, curkling of Quails, mumbling of Rabets, drintling of Turkies, frantling of Peacocks, charming of Beagles, yelling of Wolves, hissing of Serpents and wailing of Turtles."

Then there's the ambiance. Country landscapes simply are not conducive to the modern sensibility. If I could look out of my window at abandoned cars, disintegrating mattresses, or newspapers blowing through the streets, I might be able to work up a little lyrical indignation—but what kind of inspiration can I get from greensward? What a word, greensward. How would I use it in a sentence?

I suspect that the shape of my study is a stumbling block. I've been reading Goffman, Guttman, Rudofsky and Harbison concerning the impact on consciousness of shapes and spaces, and if I understand them, it's hopeless. There's no way I can write an ironical article—the only kind I know how to do—in a room with dormer windows and a beamed ceiling.

I've got to change the pictures too. My wife, in her innocence, hung my walls with Currier & Ives when what I need is a Francis Bacon, a distorted face screaming without hope, screaming at the idea of screaming, so to speak. Or a de Kooning woman, exploding with rage and sexuality, her teeth and open jaw like a back hoe.

Trying to get into the mood, I scan the titles on my bookshelves: *The Ordeal of Civility; The Comedy of Survival; God on the Gymnasium Floor; A Sad Heart in the Supermarket; Bad Mouth; Unspeakable Practices, Unnatural Acts; Bitches and Sad Ladies; Dirt: A Social History; Lying, Despair, Jealousy, Envy, Sex, Suicide, Drugs, and the Good Life.*

This is more like it. I take a looser, more ironical grip on my pencil. But there's an odd smell in the air, and so I have to run downstairs to see whether something is burning.

It's only my wife. "What are you doing home?" I ask her. "Has the entire cultural apparatus of this county come to a halt?"

"I'm baking bread," she says. "Wait a minute and you can taste it."

She looks particularly good today. She's had her hair done, in spite of the fact that she's always telling me how much money she saves by not having her hair done. She is wearing an expensive French sweater I found in a Madison Avenue boutique and a tweed skirt she picked up at a sale for only $160. Boots by Chelsea Cobbler. She always gets dressed up for cooking, which she regards as an occasion.

"Taste this," she says.

"It tastes like bread."

"Is that all you can say?"

"Like French bread. Why don't we go to Paris for a few weeks? I've got to get out of the house."

She looks me up and down, taking in my sweatshirt and jeans like a society woman sizing up a derelict in a charity facility. "Why don't you ever wear your bathrobe when you're relaxing?" she asks. "That's why I gave it to you."

"I'm not relaxing. I work at home—remember?" How can I think in a velvet bathrobe that reaches to my ankles and is decorated in an all-over pattern with Bergdorf Goodman's initials? I might as well put on a smoking jacket to review an angry novel.

Back in my study, I discover that I have drawn a plan detailing the number and placement of trees necessary for me to realize a long-deferred fantasy of swimming naked in the pool. I figure once again with the children's electronic calculator how many years of country-club dues and surcharges would equal the cost of a tennis court.

With the profound realism of a man who has a large mortgage, a leaky roof, and two moribund cars, I wrench myself back to the article. I am hesitating between equidistant adjectives when there is a knock at my door. "I'm working!" I shout in a martyred voice, but the door opens anyway to disclose my eleven-year-old daughter. She is wearing blue jeans tucked into boots, red suspenders and a work shirt. Having already lost her baby fat to ballet and gymnastics, she looks like Yves Saint Laurent's idea of a lumberjack.

"I came to give you a kiss to increase your energy so you'll make lots of money," she says. She kisses me with the sound of air escaping from a balloon. "Bye!" But she doesn't leave. She pauses in the doorway to improvise a Balanchine number on the theme of departure. After several minutes of unflagging invention, she concludes by drawing one booted foot slowly beyond the door frame.

Where was I? I try to recapture the sly thrust of my thought by standing at the window facing the road and watching a pretty young woman jog by. Despite the cold weather, she is wearing shorts and she shakes her head as she runs, as if to shake off all worldly cares. Studying her legs in a detached perspective, I wonder whether Sir Kenneth Clark would classify her as a "nude of energy" or a "nude of ecstasy."

"Guess what, Dad!" It's my thirteen-year-old son. Before I can guess, he tells me that he scored more than half his team's points in the basketball game at school. Tossing his long blond hair out of his eyes, he reenacts each play in considerable detail. "I inherited all my athletic ability from you, Dad," he concludes, to dispel the appearance of boasting. At his school, all teams are coached in apatheia, the dissembling of emotion on the field, and he comes home constipated with enthusiasm.

The dogs are barking for their after-dinner walk. My son can't hear them over his stereo set. My daughter is on the phone. My wife has gone out to give away the French bread. Maybe I need a break. Wasn't it Nietzsche who said never trust a thought that does not come while walking?

Talking to the Trades

---

*P*lumbers, carpenters, electricians and other people who work with their hands used to be strong, silent types, the sort of men who answered your questions in grudging monosyllables, as if you hadn't paid for language, too. But not anymore.

Just the other day I was talking to my plumber about my shower, which has all the force of an atomizer. "A lot of water comes out of faucets," I said. "Why can't you get it to go through the shower?"

My plumber shook his head. "It's not that simple," he said. "You're dealing with water, which is an unstable element."

"Unstable?" I said. "But all I'm asking it to do is ascend through a pipe and descend on me. Even an unstable element ought to be able to do that."

He gave me a sardonic smile. "You've measured out your life in glib assumptions," he said. "You can't predict what water will do any more than a weather forecaster can. Oxymoronic is the only word for the relation between logic and water."

Opening both faucets all the way, he studied the stream like an alchemist. "Above all things, water is spontaneous. It has a will of its own, reasons that reason knows not of. The way it seeks its own level is nothing if not romantic. Think of the thrill of rain, the lure of oceans, the purling of streams, the play of fountains."

With a poet's carelessness, he turned on the shower without drawing the curtain and allowed it to drizzle on the floor and me. He held out his hand and felt the water between his forefinger and thumb.

"You and I," he said, "emerged from water. Not only from the amniotic waters of the womb, but out of the sea, the womb of evolution. Water is the great mother.

"What is the body, after all, but water? Why is immersion so soothing, even to psychopaths? Think of hard and soft water, its moods, its *moeurs*. Water the solvent, the cleanser, the cooling agent, the dispersive medium, the catalyst."

"What about my shower?" I said. "I spent a lot of money on it, and all it does is make me damp."

My plumber's eyes flashed with indignation. "If you could see them, you would know that water molecules appear in the form of an isosceles triangle! An isosceles triangle!" He formed one with his hands, pushed it at me. "Do you suppose that this is for the express purpose of ascending a pipe?"

He picked up his bag. He had not taken out a single tool. Were there tools in it?

"No," he said with finality. "You can't do with water what you will. It's too slippery for you, too elusive, too playful. You'll just have to meet your shower halfway."

"The outside spot won't go on," I said to my electrician. "When I walk the dogs on a moonless night, I can't tell whether they're doing anything or not."

He examined the bulb, the socket, the switch, the line, the circuit breaker. "It's a mystery," he said.

"A mystery?" I said. "How do you mean, a mystery? You're an electrician, aren't you?"

He thrust the screwdriver into the slot on his belt and sighed. "You laymen are all alike," he said. "You can't bear the idea of mystery."

"What mystery?" I said. "We were talking about my outside spot."

"Your outside spot! How parochial can you be? Have you ever stopped to ask yourself what electricity is?"

"No. Why should I?"

He closed his eyes, as if to shut out the spectacle of my indifference. "Let me tell you," he said. "Let me try to make you understand." Pacing up and down, he sketched a few gestures.

"Electricity is a thrill in nature. It's the leap of the synapses on a grander scale. It's a cosmic pulse, an immanent magnetism, an embracing tension. It's flux, throb, transience."

His voice crackled with feeling. He ran a hand through his hair. "The early generators were called exciters and influence machines. They knew they had touched the uncanny."

He paused and pointed an accusing finger. "But do you know it? Have you ever felt the poetry of electricity? Listen to it! Ohms, ergs, tungsten spirals, tubes of force! Phases, lagging currents, heavy third harmonics! To flow, to transform, to generate! Electricity oscillates—osculates—between negative and positive, shiver and kiss.

"It can be awesome, too, can take as well as give life, burn as well as warm. While there is electricity in the touch of a loved one, its caress can also kill. The profoundest shudder is fatal."

"Yes, but my outside spot . . ."

He flicked the switch with a sweep of his hand. "Out, out, damned spot!" he said, and with a theatrical laugh, he was gone.

"It isn't often I get a chance for face-to-face, hand-to-hand contact," my mailman said. I had seen him arrive and had gone out to meet him.

"Ninety-one percent bills and solicitations," he said, tapping the bundle. "Gresham's law. The telephone waylays the written word."

He flourished the letters with a bitter smile. "Look," he said, "every one of them typed. Printed return addresses. Untouched by human hand. Vacuum-packed. Sterile. There was a time when it was considered impolite to type a letter, when every carrier worth the name was a bit of a graphologist. I can remember perfumed envelopes."

He flexed my mail in both his hands, as if he was thinking of tearing it up. "During the war, now, that was different. Letters meant something then. Mail had the impact of bullets or bombs. People stood out in snow and rain and looked up the road for me."

"Yours is a very important job," I said. "We couldn't get along without you." I reached out for my letters, but he pretended to sort them once more.

"Of course," he said, "there are still a few things that people won't tell you over the phone, that they prefer to write. 'I don't love you anymore.' 'I can't keep our rendezvous.' 'Please do not attempt to get in touch with me.'

"Negations. That's what the mail has come to. Nothing but negations. 'Your application has been denied.' 'We regret to inform you.' 'You will hear from our lawyers.' The humanity is gone. Why, there is even a vogue for knocking down mailboxes."

He placed the bundle in my palm, but without letting go. "Are you sure you want it? I would rather not be the agent of your undoing." He put his free hand to his forehead. "Lying in bed at night, I wonder about the people on my route. I see them crumpling foolscap in their fists.

"I didn't know, when I applied for the job. I didn't think. For who would fardels bear, if he knew that they were bad news?" Taking a rubber band from his pocket, he wound it around my mail until it snapped.

"Ah," he said, "the times have changed. To be a letter carrier you used to need good strong metatarsals. But we're motorized now and it's the spirit that cries out for support."

He seized me by the arm. He fixed me with his eye. "The requirements are different," he said. *"Mutatis mutandis.* To be a mailman now, what you need is a tragic sense of life."